QUERENCIA
AUTUMN 2022

QUERENCIA

Querencia Press, LLC
Chicago Illinois

OTHER TITLES FROM QUERENCIA

Allison by Marisa Silva-Dunbar

GIRL. by Robin Williams

Retail Park by Samuel Millar

Every Poem a Potion, Every Song a Spell by Stephanie Parent

songs of the blood by Kate MacAlister

Love Me Louder by Tyler Hurula

God is a Woman by TJ McGowan

Chrysanthemums Under Streetlights by S. Savannah Verdin

Learning to Float by Alyson Tait

Fever by Shilo Niziolek

Forgiveness is Green by G.F. Sage

QUERENCIA PRESS

© Copyright 2022

LIBRARY OF CONGRESS CATALOGING-IN-PUBLICATION DATA

ISBN

978 1 959118 02 2

.

www.querenciapress.com

First Published in 2022

Querencia Press, LLC
Chicago IL

Printed & Bound in the United States of America

POETRY

A New Deliverance – Keely Quinn (she/her)

I used to scream out
Begging you to deliver me
To bring me out of sadness
And set my feet
On the path to joy

With tears in my eyes I would declare
How I'd been in hiding all my life
How unseen I've felt
How desperately I needed saving
And I believed it
And believed that you were the answer

But now I know different
I know what you did
And who you really are
I know that the god you share
Isn't a god of goodness

The god you speak of
Is a god who wanted to hide me
To not allow the real me to shine
To prevent me from knowing,
To prevent me from seeking

The god you speak of
Doesn't love me as I am
He wants to change me
Has a prescription for my life
And a small box for me to exist in

The god you speak of
Isn't the one to take me out of hiding
He's the one who put me there
Told me I had been broken and lost
And that I needed to be better

Now I know,
God doesn't need me in a box
Doesn't need to guide my steps into tomorrow
They don't need me to fall in line
They ask me to live
They give me freedom

All those days crying out for deliverance
I was fighting against you, my keeper
Asking for something different
And not knowing to look outside of the walls
To the vastness of the real and free god

Maw I – Cristy Shaner (she/her)

I gnaw through silence, thick and slippery as sinew, but it clings
to the spit that drips from my chin.
It puddles in the sink when I brush my teeth,
and clogs my throat when I cry.

I swallow it with every meal.

I scream my voice into being,
but my mouth grinds itself to dust.
Every time I reach for lipstick, I remember
there is nothing left to paint.
When I lean in to kiss her, I can only offer emptiness.

My teeth pour into my lap
like a witch's divining bones
and they spell loss in a language as old as childhood.

Maw II – Cristy Shaner (she/her)

This scribble body rages against straight lines.
It pulses with postnasal drip and swallows bloody mucus.

I chew so hard these teeth shrink against each other.
Supreme force, high velocity, fear runs rabid in the mouth. The
jaw will only loosen under millions of years of heat and
pressure: volcanic, metamorphic.

In the center, at the tailbone, there is a wound that forever-bleeds; I
carry it like a swaddled, squalling infant wherever I go.

Its cries crack open and scab.
I am always picking at its mouth.

Empty Cup – Cristy Shaner (she/her)

I dream of faces detaching themselves and falling
like swathes of dead skin to the floor.
I dream of a man who is half beast, whose skin purples and
protrudes at the waist
where he flows into something monstrous,
and he warns me of rape and tells me to hide in the catacombs,
beneath the dead.
I dream of fingers without an owner, a hand that orphans
itself at the wrist,
that clasps my hair and tugs, and even though there are
no words, I know what the hand wants from me.
I dream of a woman who is not myself, but who lets me see
through her eyes,
and I learn she is a ghost before she does.
I dream of my father guarding a tray of heart shaped cookies, but
when he sets them down, I know he is betraying me. I dream of a
cat's claw slicing me at the navel and tearing me open till I spill.
I dream of an empty cup that will never be held, will never be
set on a table, will never be filled.

I dream of separation of the self.
I dream of displacing bathwater as I sink into the tub. I
dream of violence as routine.

after his death – Herb Nathans (he/him)

Take away my bones—what would I stand up for?
I want to lie here, a useless lump of muscle-mass.
Take away my nerve endings. I do not want the pain.
My eyes, they are useless, gouge them out quietly
and lop off both my ears. I can still hear myself cry.
Take away my stomach so that I do not need to eat
but dwell endlessly, immobile, until I am gone.
Fingertips are too delicate, probing—sever my lips
with your scythe, sew them closed. And any openings.
Slash my tendons, seesawing endlessly, let lie.
Cut out my cerebellum, the front half of my brain,
all of those memories, and the ability to think. Keep
only what is necessary, those reptilian sleepfulnesses
hidden in the brainstem's crevices. Everything else
disappears. And after all that is done? Take away my soul:
I do not need it anymore.

Swan Point – Herb Nathans (he/him)

It was a greying day in October when I finally went to the graveyard,
the name written in bold letters, Swan Point, across the white stone
at the entrance, as if it too were the name of some person buried.
Inside the rows of gentrified boxes, giant phallic monuments
of names now without meaning, despite their size.
We do not have these graveyards in California, I don't know why.
Perhaps because fewer people have died, or they are less afraid
of being forgotten. Passing by state governors, patrons of the arts,
there are enough dwelling here to build a village, or raise the dead.
But the dead do not rise. People on their morning jogs discussing
podcasts, flirting unromantically, the spot is open to the public,
more open than they know. Tracts of land set aside for future generations,
monuments listing a family name and all the children underneath.
I have an image of a father taking his son there in the dappled
sunshine, pointing to the uncut marble, the empty plot of grass,
all that the light touches will someday be yours. Not a steward
of the land but the land stewarding you, carefully preserving you
for generations to come.

Death never meant very much to me, cessation of respiration,
a flatlined EKG. Where do we go after we die? To us, there is no where.
There is no we, there is not even an is. And yet I am reminded
of harry harlow's experiment, two monkey mother facsimiles,
one with milk to feed the baby, the other offering only terrycloth
and a soft embrace, which the primate clung to invariably.
It is not soft to cling to the thought they are dead, hard as marble;
better to construct trees, memories, concepts of immortal souls
even if there is no sustenance in it, and we starve. Better to die
believing in death and its afterwards than only to cease to live,
and nothing more. And they are not unpleasing to bicycle among
and provide diversion to us all. And if they should build a thousand
cemeteries with a thousand rows throughout every town
in New England, that the dead might be never far away or forgotten,
then I say only what the gravestones say unto me: thy will be done.

airplane – Herb Nathans (he/him)

I am on a flight, traveling from nowhere to nowhere
and without any complimentary beverages, which I could not drink
anyhow.
Surrounded by strangers, I feel more uneasy than the coronavirus,
the presence of other living forms, regardless of infection.
I came here alone once before, and did not feel this scared. I do not know
what has changed, if I am averse to wintertime, if it is too late to go back.
Sunning myself under the shade of two felines, prowling the edges
of my own possibility, I may have been restless, but preferred it that way.
It is the symptom of excess enjoyment, the sloughing of our souls
like old snake skins, which we keep inside our computers like
formaldehyde
to look back on when we have forgotten we were ever a snake.
Scouring through old conversations, scowling photographs,
reacquainting myself with my own boorishness, inhospitality
to others, or to who I used to be. And ashamed, for the first time,
of my childhood, which I had always thought so perfect.
I tried on my aligners from three weeks ago and could not make
my teeth fit, they bent in all the wrong places, the opposite way,
outgrowing my own bite. And maybe it is better this way, this
gradual recognition of my futilities, fog peeling bit by bit away from
the mountain, else I would be afraid to climb. And yet it is strange,
traversing the metaphysical matterhorn without pylons, infantilized by my
credit card, a smartphone with my parents preloaded, and
that secret yearning not to climb. We do it anyhow, because we must,
driven by our own self-pride and longing and the dissolution of our past,
like an avalanche, even though we keep climbing, never reach the top.
And I ask only, swinging crazily from some sherpa who still climbs above,
impatient: is it not view enough? And how high up must I be
when I lose my footing and fall? Tonight I arrive in Providence, RI,
though Lord knows God had nothing to do with it. It is American
Airlines, and Kayak, and my mother, and the infinitudes of patience
which I provide. It is four hours and two cramped seats to land
three time zones later, the paradoxes which flying incurs, along with
unpaid insurance. We watch the drink cart hungrily, and without
eagerness,
awaiting the extent of our destiny. In some ways, we never even move.
Going five hundred miles and pacing the aisles to exercise, deep vein
thrombosis from traveling fast, by sitting still. I down two baby aspirin

and consider yesteryear under an eyemask, until even the baby
fades away. Seatbacks that never recline, except for the ones
in front of us. Plastic cups with ice in them, so as not to drink out of
the can, and then giving us the can anyhow, just for fun. Lights that
dim, turn on again inopportunely, and the captain acknowledging
the weather exists. I am not part of any of this—I am asleep.
None of this is true. I was not sleeping, baby aspirin, walking the aisleway,
there are no babies aboard. But I thought I would mention it anyhow.

It is two stanzas long with no connection in between them, it is not
nonstop, there is a layover in writer's block and a half-unwritten page.
Perhaps you cannot tell. There is a stewardess directing traffic, first
the people to Pensacola, Atlanta, then everybody else, even though
her overtime pay is insufficient to merit it. She has been to Africa
three times, and once to Antarctica, and never left the airport
except to sleep, and to shuttle herself into the back of a van.
The last day of a three-legged trip, waking up 3 am in Boston,
I do not know when she gets off. Maybe Sundays, or alternate
Wednesdays, or that hopeful day that never comes. More likely,
it is when the airline tells her, ringing her in the early morning,
you are not scheduled, roll over, go back to sleep. The plane can fly
without you. And using the white underneath as a blanket, to carry her
the rest of the way out.
I never said this story had a home base. Maybe it has no home,
making its way every day a new residence, transporting people
between yesterday's lodgings and today's. For the crew, it is a job,
for the passengers, a commute. Only a ghost of sunlight sliding in through
mostly-closed blinds. Remember, it tells the weary-eyed humans,
remember you can fly.

Party 'till she doesn't – Mia-Jo Feeley (she/her)

i

It is October & I am the clouds—hung over & red. When you drink alone there is no aftercare. I don't remember how I got home. Did I pervert the long walk or did I crash my friend's car from the passenger seat? What about the smeared makeup? What about my body? Did I make it solid or is a cloud of wine still wet while we wade through the wake of something terrible.

ii

It is the spring before & I am an atom made of empty space & mysterious nucleus. I'm sure I failed chemistry. Who can balance an equation that can't tell the difference between a scream & a laugh on the other side of a wall? "My head is all weirdly shaped" I tell my dog. I am made of the times I tell my journal it's not sad to drink alone.

iii

It is October & I am a cheap motel. Cum crusted & restless. I leak. I wreck & wreak. No one checks for weeks. Somehow, I am open for business. I am arguably the best place for foreplay on the highway, but where else are you going to go? I am the problem. That's just business.

iv

It is still alone if you are the only one in the group with a flask & I am the golden child if the skirt stays outside the kitchen. When I am drunk I am too dumb to feel anxious but too dumb to hide my grief.

v

It is a rainy morning & I am a woman made of girls that grew in the shape of their cage. I used to climb up the stairs. I used to slide into panties in the crawlspace. What did not kill me did not die. What did not kill me made me a tightrope—pulled taught across a gap. I am ready to snap. I do not.

Prayer from Galatea to Venus – Mia-Jo Feeley (she/her)

I am almost alive,
asleep, ivory yet soft,

like Hermaphroditus finally awake, an epicene caffeine machine.
Venus, let this body quake,

baleen stone to velveteen flesh.
Let model put down her prop,

let stone throb under thumb,
let sculptor pull down his bra &

come to the altar,
come to the altar.

Let flesh be woman,
Let woman covet her penis.

Venus, I come to the altar.
Let me kiss the man that makes me come
        to life, and back again.

The creek won't bring dead girls back (unless it does) – Mia-Jo Feeley (she/her)

i need to cry and it's all stuck in my throat
so i came to the creek
so much life, so much water
so much like a funeral.

all these memorial trees: a redbud named jeremy, an oak named arnold
and the unnamed ancients: mysteries the same question-mark-shape
as my grief, i am haunted by people i have not met.

let the trees be their home,
let them be red birds,
let them surround me,
let them kiss my ears,
but there's no names on the wind, no answers "who?" from the owls,
i could not even make up an omen,
        only my reflection in the creek,
        sisters crawling up my throat,
        ghosts rolling down my cheek.

Wood Queens – Helen Parker (she/her)

And the woods will tell
How we cut you down
As you made gingerbread
And stole their crowns

They just wanted to be queens
Of their own fucking age
Whilst you ripped and you stole
Took their words off the page

They took the crumbs with their hands
Built their own goddam lives
Took the stars for their own
Ignored those fantastical lies

Now they're giant beautiful girls
Nowhere near what they came from
Because what you tried upon them in hate
That power their love will be built on

So the north winds will whisper
And the rumours will spread
About how the Wood Queens came back
And sliced off your head

And they travelled the land
Past the twins, Alice, Snow White
So they could see for themselves
Together we fight.

In This Soil – Sonia Charales (she/her)

The coconut tree
Swaying with their coconut leaves
Reminds me of home

Thengende bungi
Rajyattinre ormakal

Do I belong here?
In this soil
When my roots are planted
In another nation

Theng poyal
Veedinde sookam illa
Ente veede alla
Evidai anne ente veede?

They say,
You can't plant a coconut tree
Not in this soil

Apole njan parayam
Sramikkukam
Njan sramicall
at valarum

If I make this soil my home
I can plant new roots here

Thengende bungi
Pinne ondagam

But then they will say
You can't grow a banana tree here
Not in this soil

Apole njan parayam
Sramikkukam
Ee mannil

In This Soil Translation – Sonia Charales (she/her)

Theng
Avarute thenngeyute ilakalumayi sanycarikkunnu
Veedinekkuriche enne ormappetuttunnu

> The beauty of the coconut tree
> Memories of country

Njan ivitte uṇṭēā?
Ee mannil
Ente veerukal natumpoḷ
Matroru rajyatte

> If the coconut tree leaves
> The home loses its comfort
> It is not my house anymore
> Where is my home?

Avare parayunnu,
ninnalku oru theng maram natan kariyilla
Ee mannil alla

> Then I say,
> I will try
> If I try
> It will grow

Njan ee mannine ente vittiakki marrukayanenkil
Enikk ivitte puthiya veedukal natam

> The beauty of the coconut tree
> To have it again

Pakshe avaer parayunnu,
ninnalku oru varamaram natan kariyilla
Ee mannil alla

                                          That is when I say,
                                                   I will try
                                              In this soil

Routes – Jordan Nishkian (she/her)

There are bones beneath
the hills I drive, varicose routes
running
through earth
—dark, tangled—
my eyes on the staunch cut
between gold
dry land and clear powder sky

(it's hard to neglect
the patchwork snake
of tar and ebony, or treasures
it's coiled into its sides:
plastic thrown from windows, furniture
flung off roofs,
limp bodies
of native animals,
fur and organs spilt,
open to the sun

—there are bones beneath,
ground into asphalt.)

"There are bones beneath
houses, gardens, oceans,"
the woman's voice fills the empty cabin.
There are bones beneath
passing plains:
settled, unfound.

There are bones beneath
fingers
gripping the steering wheel as I
head home
—not home—
rearview mirrors glint
with light from a dipping star.

31

The Melody of Mushrooms – Jordan Nishkian (she/her)

We've kept the fairy ring in the backyard alive
      for the last nine years, feeding it
with circles of footfall
each equinox at dusk, so

spores trickle from their gills
      planting offspring between near blades—
new stars in their cosmos,
new clouds in their nebulae—

mycelium spread strands
      of hyphae into a nexus web,
poison pulsing into soil,
ready, waiting for us to dance.

Homesick for the Campo – Ocean Tawiah (she/they)

I miss you like a plague
I'm haunted by your hidden thorns
and the sounds your rivers made.

I miss the gods I put into you
the abandoned houses I turned into shrines
I miss you in the summer
when all your plants died
and spring
when the lavender came in
and everything stayed awake
under a waxing sun.

I miss speaking into your land
sleeping under your branches
and the corners you hid
until I knew you better.

at night
as I crept out my window
to discover the delights you saved for the moon
I miss the way you held me
safe
and the sound of the wild
holding its breath
as I laid and watched the stars
that you made
after clearing the sky for me.

missing you is like loving you
loving you then was just me missing you now
or maybe it's the other way around
I'm never quite sure

all I know is this:
just like your ancient rubble becomes shrine
ageing old with wear and nature's spirit
will toss me to your wild breast weary,
ready to be reborn as something new.

03:47 am – Ocean Tawiah (she/they)

music and movement
life and heat
in a small room full of people I could know
we all love this song
or we pretend to
like I pretended to want to go out today
to like the taste of my drink
to know how to sway my hips

but it all comes back to me
with a sip and the drum of the bass
we can dance like the world is watching
and though tomorrow only leaves headaches and shame today we
are newly young.
there is beats and bodies to guide us
and a dj that tells us to
"put your hands up one more time"

and I will
guided by the strongest drink
from the nearest bar
to a remix of a remake of my parent's first dance. bumping and
grinding
shaking and winding
until _____ pulls through
and asks for my number
that I put in wrong
(of course)
and a failed drop call
makes me lock my door twice
wince at sounds downstairs and pray

35

may the paper walls
outside this home
be stronger than
a vexed man's rage.

Her New Necklace – Eric Knowlson (he/him)

They slit your throat.
Gloved hands
went in
and grabbed your glands.
Snip-snap.
They emptied you

into various jars,
labeled neatly
like malignant files:
Thyroid.
Lymph nodes.
Erroneous parts of you
cleared away completely.

They wipe your blood
for the unveiling of
a shiny new necklace
carefully clasped
back together
with simple stitches.

Which matches
the thinly woven
gown and
hairnet crown
they've scantly
wrapped around you
to be carried
down
the aisle
of shimmering
linoleum.

All the while,
the chorus
of monitors
are singing.

Back in your room
there's a knock
It's about to begin;
The after-party, that is.
"Come in!"
The nurses do,
tired, smiling waitresses
skating and serving
cocktails
to you

They all stop
to admire
your neck's
new accessory.

"Girl, that's some of the best
work I've seen"

I notice you smile;
dreamy and composed
as if behind those eyes
a part of you knows
this is but a part
you were cast to play

And why not?

You've always been fashionable,
even when it's an IV you're fashioned to

You wonder if you dreamed too much – Josephine Raye Kelly (they/she/he)

You wonder what it will be like to raise a daughter.
You're not sure if you can.

You don't know if you can wear your organs
on the outside of your skin for the rest of your life.

When you were born, someone looked at your body and
made a decision that your violation will be your vindication
because you are already guilty.

If you need an abortion, you will die and the baby that you
wanted will too because you're disposable and so were
they, and don't forget that you were responsible for the
original sin.

Now you can be subservient to a man who takes you to church Sunday mornings all smiles and handshakes, then bruises you after dinner when the evenings are too hot and his sixth craft beer is empty. Stop asking him why he smells like perfume when he's back from eighties night, where he called the bartender a slut for pushing him away after he pulled her into the bathroom by the loose threads of her skirt.

You could start counting now and it would take at least three revolutions to finish the list of men who have touched you without consent. And that's not including the men in distinguished robes who wrote the laws that sanctioned your submission. Not counting every man who wished you dead because you were not actually a woman, but a counterfeit that smelled and tasted like one.

You wonder if you dreamed too much.

Imagination is such a fragile thing.

hospital – Josephine Raye Kelly (they/she/he)

bowels of this lingering place
        halls contract and curl
                constipated
but the laxatives from the nurses
                won't purge the insides

lost in the toxins of the system
        (i thought the stairs would be easier)
          but the empty passages round each corner
winding toward an unseen ascent

ghosts of paramedics rushing up ramps
        half-conscious women
        wheeled
clinging to their klonopin
        intestines twisting
                wishing they were floating somewhere else

(all i hear is silence but the walls won't stop screaming)

        complete concrete
            devil in the fluorescents
            never-ending bland
            perpetual turns
        circling
curling   curling
        circling

footsteps
mine
        oscillation of body and thought
        hidden and crushed
the place where people wait for death
uncertain
        but refusing to eat garbage

        addicted to
something
        anything
that fills the gnawing from the incessant void

my teeth full of matches
        waiting for the flame
fooling the staff and refusing to move

captivity
        humanity
                (i'm a liability)
memories extinguished
                no sunlight
constant petty beating of my most important organ

the last sound i hear before
        someone flushes me out of the colon
behind a sign marked:
 "authorized personnel only"
        gentle tapping bottle smacking against ground

Assimilate or Die – Josephine Raye Kelly (they/she/he)

In less than
six months,
two hundred
and thirty-eight
bills were introduced
or made into law
that proclaimed:
assimilate or die.

In the pauses
between periods,
these bills said:
Your modifications
are mutilations.
Your body is
an abomination.

They asked,
Why did you
cut off your breasts?
The man on the stand
tapped the microphone
to expel the feedback
and clarified:
They were the most
beautiful thing about you.
(He insists it's a compliment.)

Perhaps we were not
loud enough
when we kicked in
the teeth of cops
at the Village.

We declare we
will not remain
misshapen diagnoses
in the DSM.

We are the medicine
that heals your
gendered wounds.
Your desperate salvation.

We will not yield
to the exhaustion
of living under a flag
that worships
a false prophet on stolen land
or a congress that legislates
our murders and calls it suicide.

The fashion of my life,
the one you mistakenly call
gender performance, will set
us free.

A Mourning Shave – Cruz Sanchez (he/him)

Swwfft! The Razor glides across my skin, *Rfft!* It takes the hairs away
from my chin, *Sfft!* I feel it rub my skin raw,
Grsttt! Until fuzz there is all.

I stop, and think to myself,
Why Should I Stop here?
What is there to fear?
If my family sees my new clean pelt?

Pushing the razor in;
There's a rush of adrenaline,
The joy, the pride,
In taking away what is masculine!

I push harder;
The Razor goes deep,
And finally, finally,
It cuts my cheek.

The Sting of blood,
Runs down my face,
Yet I don't wait,
To keep cutting up the place.

I Go faster and quicker,
Tearing skin and tissue,
Until all that's left,
Is jaw and sinew.

Oh Joy!
I say,

I am no longer man!
Finally I can feel myself becoming who I am!

Quietly, I put the razor down,
And in my sink I see
My old self starting to drown.
I am finally no longer me.

BIG HOUSE – Eaton Jackson (he/him)

I saw your house. And it was a thing of wonder, with the
sign for Those who can't see:
HOME.

Yours. Silent

Undercurrents, wrapping undulating picket fence around,
Reminding curiosity seekers, trespassing eyes have been in
the past, and will always be prosecuted,

Hanging

letterbox addendum, The money that it took

to enclosed space into an obelisk to you, That

stands center in cosmetic lawn, like a Pitbull's wrestler
stare down at any lingering eyes from across the street,

Jutting re-bars of picture-perfect, trellis for growing
tentacles for the insatiable for more pixel from the

balcony,

Of foam waves crashing against

break wall rocks hewed by that immigrants,

Thoughts of Diogenes

his also,

HOME.

constructed like yours

from inside a barrel,

Sinking Sand – Eaton Jackson (he/him)

Pretty city on

supercilious stilts,

Carving out of the mundane ocean view of
forever. Click. Click. Happy fingers on shutter like
a snappy tap dance
piano solo.

Forever feelings balanced on a

pin's point.

That the earth will hold up air-tight assumption,

Moving points in space with heavy duty equipment,

To catch earth's momentary offer of picturesque
archipelago, That plus signs were really a pluses,
And
The minuses were indicated outside of the bracket, And

x's identity was found.

Load bearing walls and all the moving

parts vying with liquid mortar for a cooling piece of crust, That if a
sudden shift in plate tectonics the parenthesis would have nullified,

The breaking up of concrete in waves,

Bent, twisted reinforcement. Bodies falling off into the

gaping nothing

where the rest of assumptions

had also fallen through.

The Official Report – Eaton Jackson (he/him)

My bleeding-pulp melanin is

An account of the incident,

Because I was there

On the ground

Leaking orifices across the street

Like oil slick meandering

towards the SPEED BUMP to

Immigrants manicuring
palatial lawns, The bleeding
congeals there,
Water cannons wash the red
road clean, My body's
account,
As I was there, me and

What was left of

ME,

In between dead and alive,

I heard the reading of the
official report of what had
really
HAPPENED,

The de-briefed verbatim

In coerced columns marching across the page.

All That Is Left of Liv – Laura Theis (she/her)

this white four-poster once
was her laughter & the darkening

night sky once was her tongue
the orangery once was a little

tear she showed no one isn't it
striking these shooting stars were

how she sneezed when
the dust came down the cashmere

I'm wearing once was her left foot
this Jasmine bush here used to be

the way she tilted her head
when not really listening those peacocks

once were her elbows the twin
dolls her headaches oh and I think

this stuffed swan was actually her heart
once but this whole country used to be

her heart come to think of it
all the cliffs & wild springs & lava fields

the unending summers the northern lights
jade flames against a black canvas

advice from one who's been burnt before – Laura Theis (she/her)

on the first day the dragon moves in
don't tell the neighbours but
take the batteries out of your smoke detector
you'll thank me later
you can stop paying your electricity bills
even asleep a dragon is more
than a room-full of candles

if you are stumped for what to feed your dragon
a little fire goes a long way
buy a multipack of tea lights
fire is what it breathes & what burns in its veins
it's also what it likes to snack on every once in a while
the way bees love to eat
honey but also make honey

oh and most important of all
if your dragon is thirsty give it verses but no water
never water but maybe a song if it is scared
stroke its wings till your hand scorches
or let it listen to the ember bloom rhythm of slow
soft breathing that rises from you like smoke
as you drift off in its glow

Medusae – Laura Theis (she/her)

Do not lose faith on the day you wake up
with spiders instead of hair.
Do not cry as you look in the mirror.
Remember: They may stay. They may not.
They are here for now.
If you must, take pains to cover your head.
Hide their crawling under your most elegant hat
lest people recoil from you in the streets.
Or don't. Remember Medusa and her snakes.
She'd turn anyone to stone if they looked at her frightened.
She was a monster and proud. All hiss, curse, and scorn: danger.

And yet to think someone must have loved her enough
to name half of all jellyfish,
those moon-glowing blooms of floating
fluorescent umbrellas and bells,

after her.

Swallow – Mimi Flood (she/her)

I think of you separating water from salt and pouring that salt in my bellybutton /I think of you tongue tying me breathless/ as if I saw the lost Atlantis inside you / I think of you in bits and pieces of love/ a soul with teeth and fingernails and burned down buildings and cheap liquor/ I always feel you like the air In between two stars/ I orgasm eggshell pearls / and put one in your mouth / and ask you to swallow.

Rekindling – Sabrynne Buchholz (she/her)

a great white egret dips low from the overcast
to weave between barren branches and changing leaves
with wishes to see rabbits before the winter comes
and what do rabbits see?

high up and just below the bough, a snare
to catch feathers and flight in a tangle of wire
and that, the rabbit sees, brings the egret from the sky
crashing to the roots of a linden tree

a train whistle blows from the spur line
the leaves of the linden in honey hues and cream
to match the fields of dent corn further down the valley slope
as the egret greets sleep under the rabbit's eye

a fox in all the reds and golds of autumn
fur in all warm pigments, spice and squash and cider
springs to life from the embers and the clay in
the undergrowth and sets its path down the
hill to see rabbits before the very first frost

what do rabbits see?
as the final convective clouds dissipate with the last white feathers
the nights stretch long
     into cool fog and lighted leaves and fox fur beneath
                                        the linden tree

At the End of Time, A Moth – Sabrynne Buchholz (she/her)

in the final throes of death, out of time, but early for the train
it rides along the line and never truly stops,
an end to all ends is not quite here yet
but still the final glimpse of a world and the
first glimpse of something unknown beyond
the realm that eyes can reach,

compound, camera type, or built in feathery scales,
all of them and all the others will only see it once,
the end of time
maybe not an ending, but a change or transformation

shed the cocoon of life
something odd is on the other side
a mystery

and there, the moth, I've laid it down in the light,
nestled low and cradled gently to greet a different
kind of tomorrow, at the end of this night, and the
call of the train

at the end of time, a moth

Year Across a Pastel Sky – Sabrynne Buchholz (she/her)

Perhaps somewhere between Eching and Munich
The sun will set on browning red leaves and final patches of
cheatgrass
To rise again on winter

    A layer of cotton from clouds in a perfect glimmering white
        It's snow! you can cry, but through his eyes and red
        cheeks it is soft

                welcoming
                  beckoning
        Cotton from eye-sockets and tears made of thread
        To weave his vision through oil and horsehair

        See frosted color-splash sky, verglas across the
                atmosphere in peach and lilac
        Wisp-clouds, cirrus, in ringlets and curls, to refract
        new day sun

Snow is sheep's wool shed in autumnal cessation and in
      counting those cusp-night dreams Dream on until
      thaw

        When cloud-dust melts off and into the river
        Cold, hibernal river

        Winter fish to flutter through current
        Like new butterflies in blue zephyr
            To carry time and drop it steady and slow

        Slowly trickle back
            To Autumn, 1907

stacy, 2:30 a.m. – Nicholas Barnes (he/him)

one light's on
but none in my room.
       i'm still awake.
i hear the mp3 and bullfrogs
syncopated like a symphony.
       curtains sway
       like closeted moth wings.
they keep out those moonbeams
like a horse blinder keeps
the blue star floatie darkness in.
       eyelids closed now,
       ready for a sound and vision show.
the hallucinatory ambush begins.
       night siren,night siren,
       meet my blurred dream sight
       and carry me till morning
       if you can, if you can lead.
but first, one question,
who are you tonight?
       a lost girl answers,
       dervishing in an emerald dancehall,
       the one where your grandparents
       squaredanced and waltzed gladly.
it was always on the drive to school.
       go there, chase that image.
she doesn't have a face,
it's a blank caul stare.
       a thin pale arm reaches through
       and grabs your hand with hers.
don't blame her, she just needs
a way to fall asleep, too.
       she pines for a partner
       to help her forget
       her woeful adolescence.
shuffle me till the sunrise,

i happily follow your steps.
        ah, there it is, slipping away.
feel the limbs start to relax,
the brain fades into dormancy,
and a warm fuzz invades.
        goodnight.
oh, and thanks for the spin.

Fiery – Prathami (they/them)

Hub, thriving center for trade
between all those different rooms
in my body, drawn out and writhing
against my face like a gong rusting
into flakes under my scalp, and my forehead shaking from
the incessant pull-and-push of worms arrayed as if by a God,

the light of the night slinks behind my eyes launching with
each foot forward a hum and thrum setting my bones a-
quibbling, like gashed trenches filled with wetness and a
bloody stink after every rain.
The red odour scrambles up m'nose and onto the trailing
ends of my fleshy curds.

The bikes outside fly by and the cars rumble along and a mosquito's
warhorn is offset only by a flood of citronella. My forehead has
been propped against a screen, and the squiggly lines
measure themselves against my loose skin. It is dirty and lined
with the grime of days past.

Heat – **Prathami** (they/them)

The car prattles on
about irrigation techniques and
how the weather hasn't been kind this year. I perch on the
edge of my knowing seat, greens and grays forcing my eyes
and
falling like wishing-well-coins
onto the bubbling floors of my gut.
The waving grass tops thrust their
brilliance into my face, they trample

over my nose and chin and don't give way to any lighter
structures.
I am waiting for the car to slow down,
I am waiting with stiffened words lodged in my collar
threatening to bake me.

a Tremor in the Leaves – Prathami (they/them)

The crickets won't shut up.
Evening breeze like a lusty sailor's belt
whipping about and soft rain drops flying
about like on little ferries of air.
Night with a tinge of heaviness, beads
springing up on your forehead like little icicle babies. The
frogs are having a gala time and the humidity chokes

oh my leaves are so strong and green and jumpy they bounce
about like ants in the sea and i don't want to stop looking at them
ho they have trapped me with their thick wrinkly lushness i am so
enraptured i am so enthused i am so happy and sorry i am so
desperate to be euthanized and they wont let me ho they the little
leaves and the large the leaves trembling with the weight the
weighted palm fronds shrugging water off like a dirty dog with
each small tremor of the air oh the farm hates me

she, of the future – Katja Warren Wild (she/her)

I want to cry between your legs
because I'm not there yet
and I want to know why.

I want to feel the vines creep from your insides
and wrap around me
with rapt tenderness.

I want to map your skin
with mine, with my fingers.
Lips, heart, tongue caressing.

Oak leaves unfurl and grow
from your nose
from the corners of your eyes.

You are home
you are holy
we are divine.
The word love was written for us
written in the animal of pure lust.

Eros doesn't live with someone who is tired of life
love does not knock on the door of a bitter, spite filled person.

We took our time, to dream, to long for each other
We had been wrapped around other lovers.
Learning our lessons
or being dropped from great heights

we had sung songs of yearning for different lives
that now wither on branches, no longer supplied
with the hope and the wishing and that beautiful companion:
naiveite!

And we met and we will meet
and we are wanting and certain

We will know when it's it
because of all the leaves
pouring from the corners of our eyes and mouth and nose
and it will feel just right

and we will hold each other and say
thank god
that was a long time stumbling around.

Returning – Katja Warren Wild (she/her)

You do not need to pierce reminders into your skin
You have not forgotten,
nor will you
that the soil under your fingernails will live longer than this species
and that it is far more important.

You do not need anyone to tell you
that there is nothing more magical than a seed
nothing with more fractal longing, more benign magnificence.

You do not need
someone else to kiss the nape of your neck
you can stand under the shower
and let the water warm you
let your blood tingle with sensation,
droplets running down your vertebrae.

You only need to let the silence scream in your ear
until you understand
she is saying "you have to break the ice
and swim out
your friends are under the trees with your clothes
waiting."

Winter is long over.

Dragon – Lucia Coppola (she/her)

The man runs through the forest and approaches the stream.
Out of breath, he holds a bloody hand to his heart
years of escaping high tides, heavy rainfall, the city.
He doesn't see me, but from the field
I see his pace weakening. And I see that she is chasing him,
a hurricane blast of a harridan's spray, with jagged green
scales propelling currents and the darkening day.
Does he know she's coming?
Does he see her there?

I remember him when he was a child.
He played in the playground like me, and she was a beauty
who showed promise as a folk singer with magic dragon
songs before the downtown job made her weary from sweat
and fog, before pipelines and trawlers fracked her out of
a home and into the sea. How else could it be
with those schemes they'd devised
to foreclose on other people's dreams?
That's when slime developed on her hands and knees,
when the boss stopped paying her a living wage
and his yearly taxes.
That's when we knew we were doomed,
we bug-eyed tadpoles
that had sprouted from her womb
in one form or another.

Dragons shift shape with tides and seasons. This one's from
New York Harbor but could be from Singapore, Ann Arbor,
as all of her kind would be stars if the tides had drifted
otherwise, if we her children had watched out for her and
seen the sludge encrusted claws grow with the urban sprawl
the leviathan's roar she suppressed though she had
sent warnings to us nicely with a seaweed tainted smile
about limits to growth, she was saying for a while,
if only we hadn't abandoned her in a mire of

64

unopened bills and letters, the smell of urine on her legs,
sour, as she went slumping sluggishly into the harbor, ankles
bloating, and nursing her wounds
this mother of ours.

Out from the woods, the man approaches now. He carries
a boy that carries a toy. It's a sword that looks ready
for battle. He falls to his knees and feels the breeze
of northern glaciers melting. The dragon's breath
rolls in on the grass toward the stream with a language
that's born of betrayal and a primal scream.
Unsuspecting, he washes off the sweat and blood,
cups his hands and gives water to the child.
"What are you going to do?" I implore.
"Nothing" he says, "Camp here for a while
then tomorrow go farther."
And that's when the winds of her anger blow
even harder. "He understands nothing!" she roars,
and everywhere it pours.

Green – Lucia Coppola (she/her)

she-wolf mongrel
urchin girls on a pile of newly raked leaves
as if we'd just graduated from childhood
our eleven years squinting into the overcast day
thoughts hazy as chocolate powder stirred up in the cup
clever at chimerical readings of fortunes in each other's palms
talk of God still very much up in the clouds
though soon our faces would search
in embers at the fireside the way to admit
wanting to study the Gospels and the Psalms to know
that truth in Aramaic is sharira and ehmet in Hebrew
the hope that nothing stays hidden past the smoke
back at the time of fallen leaves how you would always
beat me at tic tac toe and I would wear a green sweater
that my grandmother had knitted for me how
your jeans looked like hand me downs from your brothers
but most importantly how good we were at cartwheels
walkovers and playing hide and seek when it rained
games of chance or jacks and inventing dances
in the bleak sun and chill that weekend in White Plains
where bare branches drew jagged lines on sky
crossed paths with crows that chanted plaintively
what neither you Tracy nor I barely noticed back then
but hear now faintly echoed in the memory of our girlhood
long entangled hair those leaves all over the ground
on the cusp of blowing into rusted watering cans
by the patio with rain and silt of something becoming new and
with the distant rush of the Sprain Brook Parkway
modern river at Jericho clear and running over
we had not yet begun to experiment with color contrasting
red and black as winter would struggle with the allure
of purple playfully biting its tail in search of verity
and little did we know just then seated as we were
on that pile of leaves that Sunday as the photo was being
taken of us that never again would we ever be so green

Medusa – Dorothy Johnson-Laird (she/her)

you call me Medusa
but do you know the power you've just unleashed in me, there are
snakes rippling out of this head

watch out,
I'm wilderness unchecked, untouched
impossible to contain

I'm a flame, a burst of light, the sudden beauty of dark sky

you can't catch me, cage me, burn me

I'm Medusa
an old woman still young, wise to your words,
afraid of no-one

Your Power is the Rain – Dorothy Johnson-Laird (she/her)
Dedicated to Funmilayo Ransome-Kuti

Her power moves through the wind
Funmilayo turning in the earth, sky, and stars

She has a force that is fire
She scatters wind through the open sky
She has a force

I was asleep, resting in weakness
And your eyes moved through me
Your eyes moved inside me
I am no longer dreaming

Your power wants to tell me a story
Your power speaks to me
I am no longer afraid

You pushed me, I cannot be weak anymore
Strong spirit
Your rain pours over me and I am renewed
Your rain power is on me

I am still
You have come to shake me
I am still
Your eyes see inside my spirit
I am still
But you won't let me alone
Your power
Funmilayo
Your power is the rain Funmilayo, your power is the rain

Permanence – Evan Violets (he/him)

there would always be a sort of translation
revolving around the pre-dominant characteristics
of reminiscing, clinging onto a memento,
a representation of familiarity, of remembering.

there also existed an absence of reasonable origin—
nothing truly pointed to the concealed catalysts
of nostalgia brewing.   these indefinite
extents of missing, we had no proper epicentre
of which we could assign the blame, this blame.

this missing arising from harboured (in)action,
this clawing sensation redefining regret.
this missing tumbling heaps of bitterness,
this suffocating helplessness, a desire for
          another chance...

this missing slotting into state of no possible estrangement,
un-abandonable chapters—   un-withering
through the stretches of time.   missing as medals,
as plural showings we flaunt,

these statures of unaged permanence.

(SKY)SCRAPER – Evan Violets (he/him)

we'd peaked at our most impromptu black horse moments,
        snatching the slightest victories from imperceptible
        positions—   the days vested in the normality,
        the neighbourhood-ness. there was no determinable
        starvation of limelight,   just that rather self-explanatory
                and   seeded inferiority complex
        (mathematically) plotted somewhere to maximise the
        tremors of internal havoc.

we'd peaked as pockets of unmistakeable youth, as
        uncultured naivety ripe in the line of fire, shatter-able in the
        most fool-proof of ways. our bull-like instincts, aged thriller
        film storyline deprived of suspense whatsoever.   we
        stood out in the occurrences when we'd supersede their
        pre-assigned boundaries / expectations, that'd all fade with
        time, i guess...

we'd peaked as relentless dream chasers, marinated in
        resistance against other possible routes, locked in the
        wanting of the highest altitude. the path to the summit
        curtained with illusionary inability we'd have to fight
        through, self-portrait becoming an expression of figurative
        littleness.

when / if we set foot on the summit,
would the many climaxes enroute slip into a delocalised
condition,   would we forgo the footsteps taken?

Our Pretend Implodes – Evan Violets (he/him)

i stray into the devious midnight,
with no sapphire-saviour hands to
salvage the ghastly timelessness
that'd become my centrepiece

      my centrepiece—

albeit the fact that nothing could
make this collection of haunting-
simmering-rue any more divine.

we orbit around a scenery so irrational,
so magnificently dilapidated, so intricately
grim, and in the same ominous kind of
syncing,   we see ourselves
rippling in the frame of all the dreaded
aftermaths (that'd reek of all but happily-
ever-afters)

all our distant dreams, irrelevant–
silent. (not a silence we choose) a
silence etched into the perimeters
of the universe.

we've sobered up from all the ways
we've hidden from the truth of
everything. we tried to feign an
ignorance, but all our pretend
implodes, and we're left to see
the world bare in its agonies.

Dressing for Narciso – Jo Bahdo (they/them)

Your words parting your mouth as ashes
grounding heavily, entangling, suffocating
covering like your shadow, a temporary tattoo
leaving traces of now burnt cinnamon freckles
on my skin and shape, akin to yours and cursed
for the dresses on the door and the bedroom floor
only worn on your delicate days to hush my guilt
as one more smile carved another scar

Severed – Maryam Imogen Ghouth (she/her)

"I look at you and see him:
your eastern brows, your thick locks,
the way you leave trails of sticky notes
and dot the room with cold teacups;
I see the day he took you from me when
even Margaret Thatcher couldn't help me.
I see it all over again."

She tells her daughter
the same story she's told her every year:
"He chained me to a bed and then..."

When the daughter removes the lamp
from her room, the room in which she
scatters notes and dots teacups,
her mother tells her:
"This is not your home."

Her daughter pleads: "I came back
years ago, but you still see only
my father's shadow."

When the daughter is bedridden, hospital-bound,
her mother, through a throng of spirits
oozing from her outstretched lips, says:
"I must dash to a party because I want to..."
Her daughter mutters: "Have sex."

And when the daughter moves to a foreign land,
her mother emails every six months;
she does not text because it costs
two pounds:
two pounds of hope.

A mother protects herself from

her love for her child.
She cannot bear to suffer loss. She
cannot bear defeat
to two palm trees and a sword,
and the guilt
of not rescuing her child
from a man who shackles and beats so

she cuts the cord.

He Was Also – Maryam Imogen Ghouth (she/her)

This man's polarity reminds me
of Ted Bundy—the man
who killed women,
but saved a toddler from drowning
and volunteered
at a suicide hotline.

This man,
with his kindly hands,
knitted a scarf for his daughter;
he loved her and could not bear her shiver;
the respiratory spasms in her little lungs
rode him like guilt on wire.
"Breathe my darling" he'd say,
"Breathe, I am here."

He held her palpitations in his palm
as if she were a nestling, fragile, jittering,
and wrapped the woollen round her
and pummelled his wife's eyes
with knuckles stretched like lace;
he thrashed her face,
but made her feel unforgotten,
a queen supine, wet with love and pulp
like an oyster drawing from the water column.

He was also loving.

He choked his daughter with his hands,
then nursed her when wheezing
and beat her mother thin,
but fed them both full.

He was also.

All I See is Red – Jo Bahdo (they/them)

The onesie you bought me a couple of Christmases ago
too tight, an invite to lose weight
and once everything started to fit too lose
your anger tinted your cheeks in just the same hues

Blending and *bleeding*

Too much, not enough, too soon, not right
my body suffered your mood swings
malleable like an accordion
unable to reach a high pitch

In my nightmares you invite the spiders in
throwing them at me, screaming of pleasure
while I whisper fear, wisps of warmth
condensing against my insides

Becoming *terra firma*

Unable to yield half a heart
half my guilt, in persisting we perish
although I came from your womb
from two different worlds, we gloom

Pañuelo (Handkerchief) – Angela Acosta (she/her)

I was raised the Anglo way,
didn't know about Day of the Dead
or how to set marigolds on an altar.

I have lost no one but my own heritage.

Friends brought forth souls I'd never known,
from Guanajuato, from Los Angeles,
from some ancestral home never mine to claim.

I received a *pañuelo*, a handkerchief, for Easter.

When we held a virtual ceremony in 2020,
I shared my *tartarabuela*'s *pañuelo*,
holding it like a rope between generations.

I cannot grieve my departed ancestor
but I will always remember that the past
visits us in familiar ways too.

Casa Italia (Marinara Fingers) – Gina Bowen (she/her)

Little fingers against tall tables, wide
fishbowl eyes peering upward
at the women of the family
stirring the pots, and stirring the pots.

*(Sunday sauce. Marinara blood dripping
from their hands.)*

Their crimson sang songs of papers and boats,
of house work and hard work.

The provolone had a seat at the table.
It would stink
like the rancid tobacco
from the cigar puffs caking the patio.
And from a steaming kitchen, I'd watch them
refill the wine, and refilling the wine
with marinara fingers and stricken voices
once backhanded to them, in knowing of their place.

*I am to be seen and not heard.
We are to be seen and not heard.*

I absorbed servitude like a sponge.
Servitude, the garlic:
heavy-scented, earthy, and staining.

And within our steaming kitchen
I watched the women move their marinara finger snakes.
And, in defiance of predetermined womanhood,
I licked the blood from my fingertips.
A refusal to make sauce
for forthcoming Sunday evening dinners.

Thoughts on Lost Girls – Gina Bowen (she/her)

I think it is entirely possible that lost girls can submerge back into the earth a recovering addict. / Someone who has abandoned the desperate aching for their mother's womb / and has felt the enamor of Neverland wear off. / All that becomes truly dead is their denial. / They can return home: full grown, blossomed, and reborn. / Their sins can be held funerals somewhere beneath Mermaid Lagoon, / honored and dressed in pearls their watery hands had collected from clam shells. / While accountability is taken for each of them, / and they are given seaweed wrappings to wind around their hair. / It is a soft reminder to be worn as badges: / This is who they were. / This did not define them. / This is not what they are. / Nor is this what they will become.

I think it is entirely possible fairy dust can grow with each gentle breath of the lungs. / That is the magic that lost girls will find they own within themselves. / Their repentance and resilience are what allows them to see the second star from the right and return home. / Home to soft, quilted coverlets upon beds and parents sleeping but one door away from their weary heads. / Heads that are no longer consumed in darkness, overtaken by pirates, and pressed deep into purgatory. / Heads that will take what has been planted and open to blooms of rose petal and willow-bark. / Things that will not only show signs of life but create it. / Things that will keep the shadows at bay and their own darkness clinging to light; / light that has now burst forth to complete them as whole. / What was once pronounced dead will now be announced new life.

And I think it is entirely possible for nursery doors to remain wide open to the realms of possibility and imagination, / while allowing what was once lost to be found, / and to open to the stars that assure / that the best of women are those who had been reborn, / called back from the dead, / and been given the life-altering gift of flight.

If We Were Moths – Gina Bowen (she/her)

Transfixed to flame:
white, stark,
pallid in color.

We ghost around the orb,
a fluttering desperation
on dull, dark, and soundless days.

Trying to reach,
trying to touch,
but flailing, failing,
                  stuck.

The undying:
Dancing with death.
Thumb-tacked to loose shingles
sitting upon a foundation that was
never standing more than it lie sinking.

Dead-cast and shedding shells,
forever gaping in our grieving.

Planet XX – Jillian Calahan (she/her/they)

The female body is like a planet
you can't help but orbit.
Her soft skin a road map
to places you've already been
and places you have yet to discover.
But there are parts of her that scare you,
parts you can't control,
because they are parts
that don't belong to you.
None of her belongs to you.
And yet you feel the need
to pollute her,
and destroy her,
as you hide behind laws
you've written to "protect" her.
Laws that could kill her.
But do you feel that?
The earthquake that shatters her heart?
Her anger, red hot like magma.
She'll stay silent no more.
So don't be surprised when the lava
pours off her tongue
in a volcanic eruption
that will bury men in ash.
Welcome to the extinction.

Triggers – Jillian Calahan (she/her/they)

I woke up this morning
with less rights to my body
than a gun.
It is no longer enough
to have a heartbeat.
And if we're being honest,
for a woman,
it was never enough
to begin with.
If only my uterus
had triggers,
maybe I would be worthy
of protection.

Streetgod – Dee Allen. (he/him/his)

Hearing the sound
Of sirens blaring
From the street
Doesn't guarantee me
A feeling of security.

Give a thug
A badge and
He'll swear
He's a powerful
God over the street.

Strutting like Ares,
God Of War,
Rising into real-time from pages of ancient Greek mythology.

Loved by none,
Hated by everyone.
Trained for war,
Living for carnage.
Whenever he can

Prove his point.
Legitimised
Enemy to the people. Who else
Would leave

Empty shells
From fired bullets?
Puddles of blood
On the pavement?
Fear of death in our hearts?

Knee in the back,
Knee on the neck—
What's the difference?
However they're done,
Submission holds are brutality.

High-fives and amens,
Like waterfalls, descend.
Admired for his warrior mindset. Anointed a lord
Among uniformed vermin.

He's the main reason
Black fathers, Brown fathers Give their sons and daughters The
Talk—on proper behaviour. The boogeyman wears blue.

He's the main reason
Non-White
Lives are stolen
Every 28 hours (I would say less). The reaper uses a Glock.

We could feel justice
Slipping through
Our fingers
In this historically
Racist country

With at least
13 or 1300
Of his sort, working in precincts. Quarrelsome city-stormer
Hunting for pretexts

Anyone in the city could be next for the trigger pull,
Kill at will,
Decreased community,
Body bags to fill—

Children have a right to be scared. Adults have a right to be scared.
Citizens have a right to be scared. And a right to live free
From the fear on which he thrives.

Oppose
The self-ordained
God over the street
Even I
Wouldn't bow to.

(For Rosalynn J. Diaz.)

Saint George Floyd – Iwuagwu Ikechukwu (he/him)

Eighteen-eighty-six was a whirlwind of woe

Mama Africa's rind mutilated; her ova scattered upon distant soils—
sprouting unknown

Then the kneecap of suppression quenched the booming flame

And covered its embers with a pall of Golgotha ash

Earth moved from its axis

Grief was the force, anger was the flair

Perhaps not the first of its sordid kind

For the Vatican wields no monopoly in nepotistic awarding of halos

Mother earth couldn't agree more—together with the wilting wind

The shrunken sun and nostalgic mien of flowing waters

Above your cranium sits not the hangman's noose

But a halo by God bequeathed;

Vox populi—vox dieu*

*voice of the people is the voice of God

Untitled – Talya Jacoby (she/her)

The beggars I can understand
Not the ones with the signs
Cold and hungry, God bless
But the ones coming up too close to your face
Daring to ask for change
I too am asking
My words are just better dressed
They smell better
They are easier to digest
But trust they despair just the same
They are just
As easy to ignore
Roaming the streets with no destination
They are a skeletal man wearing a Greek toga
You only notice the visible ribs
And know he is full of asking
You cross the street
Avoid eye contact and mostly you avoid asking
Yourself, society
Hands covering the ears
Fingers plugged in so hard they leave a dent
Don't hear, don't listen
Question marks rattle in your pockets
Like spare change
Like change is free

Untitled – Talya Jacoby (she/her)

I wear my weathered hair like a clue
Untamed strands of neurosis
If pulled I might just unravel
Because my winsome face gives nothing away
Small hands that hold your burdens, busy carrying
Fingers that point in all directions but the home of blame
Vast rooms, empty chambers
A precious stone cold calcified heart
Can you not see I am petrified?

Things – James Piatt (he/him)

I wonder about things,
twigs glued to a piece of wood
floating downstream in a lazy brook,
a brook that meanders
into lost memories and never returns,
a bird stamp on a letter to someone
I once knew, years ago,
but who is now dead,
a homeless lady sitting
on a wooden bench knitting
an imaginary shawl, in a mall,
waiting for dreams that will never unfold,
like hopes that never unfold
into reality,
a reality that is too dark and painful,
the newspaper's ink that shapes
the early hours with issues and letters
to the editor
about a clown that lives in a house painted white, white as the
world
in which he envisions
his virtual imaginary life,
where he runs barefoot through sand,
that covers crimson lies
that are a façade for something else,
something else that consumes
his mind as it drifts into unreality,
and which takes too many with him.
I watch the sun's beams that cover
the wharf standing atop briny scrolls
hiding answers in the teal-colored waves
that refuse to take off their salty shoes
to wade on the graves of sea urchins
that taste like Chinese paper,
Chinese paper that wraps around symbols

of things lost a long time ago,
and which could hold answers
to things unknown.
I dab my eyes and shift my gaze
to the corners of the black-crusted poles
holding up the pier,
the pier which in its darkness
covers the hopes of those who are lost
and continue to move back and forth
with the tide, like things ebbing and merging
in my mind, my mind
that is filled with incongruities and aging thoughts, thoughts about things
I do not understand,
yet I continue in my hope
for some clarity,
to question those things
that are seemingly unanswerable
and unknowable.
There is a cardboard sign
on the pier that says, no wondering here,
here in this place where the sun shines
across the briny water,
and licks the hours with its encrusted tongue.
I kick the sign,
stomp on the fibers that remain, and sigh,
sigh as if I had only a few hours
left in my life,
to find answers to those things.
I look at my lists of things
and ponder on those that
after a lifetime of searching,
still remain unknown,
and count the eyeballs and teeth in the darkness that stare and
gnaw at my questioning mind,
a mind that is slowly
consuming years and memories,

memories that pile one upon the other
like the years that crawl atop each other
in the mad race to die;
as I continue to carry the burden
of never knowing all those things,
things that seem to make no sense
in a world that makes no sense,
in a time which makes no sense.
I watch the sunset disappear
into the crimson line
that separates me from eternity
and wonder, and watch, and watch,
waiting for someone
sitting in the crimson fire
of the far horizon
to tell me about those things
I do not understand.

"Tramps" – Margaret D. Stetz (she/her)

Because they hated me
because they were older sisters
of girls who hated me
because they hoped
to see my body purpled
with punishment
and just *because*
they told their mothers
to tell my mother
that I had called them
"tramps"
      a word
I held between my fingers
turned over and over
but could find no way in
      tramps were men in rags
who carried sacks on sticks
Emmett Kelly the Clown
"Weary Willy"
begrimed and bearded
with teardrop eyes
wise in the ways
of freight trains and campfires
      these weren't
girls who slept
outdoors
why would I
call them hobos?
riding the rails
feeling the rush of air
the heat of mulligan stew
warmed in a tin can
careless of appearance
of clothes
of dirt

drinking from flasks of freedom
did girls ever do this?
         not these girls
with their coats
of pink nail polish
tight pedal pushers
eyeliner like wings
rising to nowhere
stranded in groups
on concrete front steps
the hoods of cars they couldn't drive
imprisoned by fear
of words that made no sense
like "tramps"
         but they were right—
I'd watched them
looking for
and looking at
my future
feeling weary weary

Trefoiled – Margaret D. Stetz (she/her)

They hoped to make me *uniform*
that green dress
inscrutable pictures on badges
to stop me smashing
on plaster walls
more fragile than my skull
a head so bored so bored
with everything but the Guiding Light of TV
(soaps game shows afternoon cartoons)
to get me
friends
       in the school basement
metal folding chairs
laid over black and yellowing
linoleum squares
the Troop sang
with no piano
no common key
in sullen rounds
of promises engraved
upon the heart
(how
could I engrave
on my internal organs
and would it hurt?)
       their song appealed to me
the mystery of "whene'er"
"Whene'er you make a promise"
(words forced to sacrifice
their letters
still retain meaning—
worth remembering)
       in the windowless room
doubling as bomb shelter
the red-faced woman

who called herself
Leader
handed out needles
and silky thread
a square of gauze
with an outline
like the head of Mickey Mouse
like mutant clover
like a cloud with dropsy:
Trefoil.
        confined below stairs
nowhere to scout
I was a girl
and Fate said to sew
(or *embroider*
which sounded harder
and always is)
as in a fairy tale
chains
would not be struck off
until the Witch
had my Trefoil
covered in green stitches
soaked in my blood
        all afternoon I worked
messily landing outside the lines—
trochees, where spondees were needed—
able to stand no more
I stood
my Trefoil rising too
bound to my skirt
fabric to fabric
inextricable
unless I ripped one or the other
to shreds
        the tittering laughter of girls
(not friends)

the Leader's red face swelling
I was scouted out
          but from this
a lesson to keep
a promise
engraved upon my heart—
always to make
lines of my own
to bleed into them
embroider them
howe'er
I wanted
whene'er

Drowned Slaves Rise 1781 – Katherine Leonard (she/her)
On hearing M. NourbeSe Philip reading Zong!

      Tis the ancestors breath. In the voice of the waters. Birago Diop

When she gives Voice

    Sound
            Calls us to her

Water   surrounds our   parts
                           Spirit
            Rises into

Names
      we called ourselves

      Names went on with survivorkin

Lost to writing
      We were
          cargo

Excess baggage overboard
      Black

Black Ivory
           Arms
     Heads   Legs
  Torsos

Male
   Female
      Ditto Ditto Ditto
        and one Meager Female on the manifest
Manifest our destiny

Property thrown to the sea
        Lawsuit

NourbeSe speaks

NourbeSe speaks

Speaks
      of them   of us
           for them   for us
              with them
with us

Through her throat
      Arise through sea
          All Zong Arise

 all ship's cargo all

NourbeSe drowns with them with us
      with them us
         us through her

Arise as Sound
      Parts waves
         Parts Time

Time
         rejoins true names sounded

Spirit draws back
     the
         Silence

"Breaths" - words Birago Diop / music Ysaÿe Barnwell, Sweet Honey
in the Rock

The Washerwoman Loses Her Mind — Katherine Leonard (she/her)

She meant to clean out goop and grit fouling the works.
Gray cumulonimbus waves in her brain.
She can get the blood out of shirts and sheets.
Oil and tar move under her swollen, red, nimble hands
Resembling meat hooks with a tender edge.

Mechanically adept, she understood how to unscrew
The top of her head. Delicately, like a silkworm weaving,
She removed the brain and observed the gray matter
Swarming like bees. Angry. Vengeful bees.

The all-purpose cleanser and hydrogen peroxide with a good rinse.
Brain all washed. Then dried at low heat.

     But
While carefully degreasing those pesky crinkles, she lost a few.
Brain re-inserted, the world looked cleaner. And much, much
simpler.

Reweaving the Web Between Us – Katherine Leonard (she/her)

Our bond frayed in its core that day you said how hard
it was for you to find the man you married
so many years before

Hanging
        from a rope thrown over the beam in the living room.

You–came out in the morning to see him there–stark and definite–

 You stepped into an eternal night both of you shared
        when he stepped off that chair.

You said to me,
        "All I could do was just hold him"
        and I left you in that place

You sat next to me as we drove.
I could not
        did not respond.
All I wanted was for the horizon to come close
        and the earth to be flat and us to drive.
Anywhere other than there.

You are in a different world now,
and sometimes I think I can hear you,
        but I have to listen in silence

        where space becomes thin between us

and all I can do is hold you.

In Front of Misery – Ken Been (he/him)

I hesitate
in front of misery
and cross the street.

They let out early
into the iron snow
the curb is crumbling
salted, revealing its atomic stone
an underworld of gravel and sand
elemental sadness, base torture.

I keep my distance and close off my airways—
they are contagious
their droplets eject
fall to the street
unsweepable.

The broth I force down has a picture of a sad chicken on the can
it depresses me spoon after spoon
my blood saturates with its fat-bubbles; suffering floats,
my immunities abandon resistance.

They orbit the barrel
like officiating forces
raising their right hand
hot with rag flames
that singe familiarity and touch off their palms
I sniffle and they look up.

I pick up a stone and pose to throw
a warning
a fear response
fight or flight
they surround me
I am their barrel, their dance, their sadness,
repression-crushings like pottery dug from the shambles of earth.

I open my palm and
drop.

I sit on the curb
waiting
a kid in a striped T-shirt
sworn into sorrow.

Full Moon – Karen Carter (she/her)

A full, gold-tinged moon
soaks my skin
like a sliver of citrus hangs
on my tongue
from a bite of intense dark
blood orange chocolate.

The memory of this moon haunts me.
I must trust its bitter potion.
My front porch sitting after teaching school
empties my mailbox.
Stored-up grief deposits orange lines,
streaks across the sky before daylight.

The rainbow after a storm
does not calm me
as does the moon's orange ball.
It steadies my driving
home after a late-night dinner.
A fly pesters me while I steer.
It cannot find my left-overs
in the Styrofoam box.

I am left with mysteries
even fresh-cut grass
cannot explain or create
a fresh start.

What a long night it will speak.
Trust the heavy load
from the tender hand
that holds sacred tears
falling down
from the moon's glow.

The Unseen dashes gold pouches
on dry, brown leaves,
before the sun goes down,
dies to another day.
Twigs blow across
my front porch, as gnats look
for a place to land.
Time exchanges light for dark.

7/9/22 – G.F. Sage (she/her)

I am not healed / I am bandaged / I haven't stopped the bleeding
underneath / I've stopped the spreading / you would not believe
how the sound of a laugh / could send me into a spiral / how the
mention of him / depletes the air from my lungs / how I'm telling
you it gets better / it does / but I can't tell you when it's over / I
don't know that it's ever over / where this book ends my story is still
being written / I am still becoming / still replaying / reliving the
moment's I've misplaced in my mind / it's like making sense of
objects in a dark room / like inkblot's on paper / or jigsaw pieces
clicking together / I may not find all the pieces / I might never be
whole / I may not always be living / but I am alive /

I am alive

Somewhat Together – G.F. Sage (she/her)

I am held together by promises made under the moonlight

Retract the blade, you cannot carve out his touch from your skin.

Held together by my mother's hands, wrapped around me, as I stain her shirt with my downpour.

You need to accept yourself for who you are and stop wishing you were someone else.

Held together by lists of reasons to walk this earth a little longer

Rainy days, car rides with friends with the windows down, always wanting to be some kind of writer, and your little, happy fluff of a dog's face when you come home.

Held together, not always quite together as planned

A vase shattered on the floor, gluing the bits and fragments that didn't fall under the darkness of the fridge. Some gold leaf here and there to showcase there is something beautiful in the way we break, and rediscover ourselves.

Constant Reassurance – G.F. Sage (she/her)

Do you think you could always love me?

I don't ask but I wonder, as I flip through my clothes noticing half of my belongings once belonged to her. The decorations on my walls of pictures she's painted, the notes I've kept in a heart-shaped box, and even the beauty I've found in myself are all reminiscent of her.

There is a darkness that looms inside my chest, a pulling that splits my ribcage apart in the after hours. Letting my heart fall from me and onto the floor, thrashing around like a fish out of water. And as it squirms it also weeps, "Please be the one. The one for me, and the one who stays..."

Losing you would mean halving myself into bits over and over, until I am so minuscule that I could be confused for ashes or dirt. And I would rather be burned or buried alive than ever be forgotten,
but somehow, I can't escape the feeling that I might just be a burden.

Balcony – Laura Holt Andersen (she/her)

I'm still on that balcony
all cement and metal, babe
reflecting the grayness of you and I
hard as a rock, but all dusty and dry
little specks of sand
slipping through each other's hands

The rain could have sealed us
but the balcony veiled us
brought us together in vain
because we never said anything
missed out on our glue
got the chance, but fell through

But I'm still on that balcony
all cement and metal, babe
wanting to kiss you
waiting to kiss you
waiting in vain forever, just missing you

And no one ever knew
least of all you

Worshipped mythology – Laura Holt Andersen (she/her)

I made an archangel out of you
an ancient god, if you will

I know it was less than what I portray
but I still can't help but think the two of us reigned
could've ricocheted
into royal fames
fight ready for the games
of all the battles in the faded frames

Hallelujah hymns
praying for our love's win
I saw the signs on all the banners
our symbol symbolic of all that matters

Oh, I could've given you
anything worth risking losing
I know we're just regular humans
but our love story could have severely ruled

A king and queen
or Lilith and Lucifer
Roman or Greek
we'd be worshipped mythology

No Matter the Roses You Bring Me Now – Fatima Riaz (she/her)

If the sky calls upon me
And pulls my breath away;
And I, by your side,
No longer stay
But the love for thee,
Will forever be.

If tomorrow's Sun didn't open my eyes,
May you lead a thousand cries
And regret for weaving the truth,
A little less.
I would not return.
Though to caress your tears.

If tomorrow's breeze touch'd my face,
A cold blow.
The spring unfold'd but the gardens,
Refus'd to bestow!
No matter, the roses you bring me now;
I weltered long ago.

If tomorrow starts without me,
And yet I keep turning my head
In search of You, calling my name.
At least come,
Come! One last time
See me turning into dust!

How Kids Contend with Boredom – Valerie Wardh (she/her)

a.

scoot   a shoe

      across   the rug

rub free its coppery musk

peel sweaters apart, the crinkle and
       cling

touch wood paneled walls, deep-
       grained grooves

or touch metal surfaces

      and snap

b.

our room is a mess of plump pillows

encased in corduroy

we wallow on them

slipping t-shirts off our bodies

the bean bag crunch

dry friction of a VHS tape

slotted squarely in its mechanism

blare of television slurry,
      disney ballad

we eat stale popcorn

kernels pooling, oily beads

c.

My cousin and I put her toys on trial.
We strung up their jointed bodies
          with rubber bands
and delivered a verdict.

She scissored the hair
off their guilty heads, lit candles
and watched
the chemical process
by which synthetic strands burn.

I dismembered barbie,
limbs as slim and rubbery
as hotdogs, piling them
in the corner: long sentence reduced
to a jumble of phonemes.

Content with our work,
we wrapped ourselves in the
          bright nylon of
sleeping bags. *Don't fall
          asleep yet*,
she said, threatening to poke me
with a detached doll hand.

The Backyard of the Rental Home We Won't Be Able to Afford Much Longer – Valerie Wardh (she/her)

we recline on plastic patio chairs, ignoring
the abandoned wasp nest four feet away
dark clutch of sockets anchored to the eaves

a gap in the wood fence is wide enough
for a doberman's snout to push through
snarling at our fresh-cut grass
or perhaps at the overgrown bush
that waves all its limbs in a silent cry, *hosannah*

there's something enchanting
about the neighbor's unkempt lawn
with its knee-high forest of baby's breath
weeds and saplings erupt
along the property line, where we can't or won't mow

Portrait of an Exurban Family – Valerie Wardh (she/her)

I sat, inert, in the house they had found
in the hills, had selected proudly for its
isolation, for its all-but-unreasonable commute
to the nearest city center. Dad was grafted to the recliner, flipping
channels on the TV that he'd mounted
some years ago on a large wall shelf
between porcelain knick-knacks, antique cameras,
and a few untouched books about spies.

He deftly skipped past the movie channels,
pausing only briefly for a war film
(he grunted with distaste that it was not
in English, put-upon at having to read subtitles)
and kept jamming his thumb
against the button until the screen displayed
Bob Vila's inoffensive face, placidly delivering
guidance on the grouting of tile.

Nope, seen this one before, Dad said
with a comedic affectation. Mom looked
up from her laundry basket across the room,
clucked in acknowledgment.
When he landed on an infomercial
for a zucchini slicer, he called out dramatically
to no one in particular: *Yuck, no thanks.*
I don't eat vegetables, and changed the channel.
Mom hooted like an owl and cackled
like a gibbon. Certain I had missed
something, I prodded, *Why's that funny?*
to which he retorted, *It's funny because*
it's true. Mom snorted, then applauded him
with the fervor of a circus seal.

On the national news, talking heads began
their steady sermon. When a rogue comment

slid out, misaligned with his clean-cut philosophy, Dad
shouted down the newscaster, who I supposed
was used to it by now, and would
continue undeterred with their report,
indifferent to his chair-bound raving.
Mom barely noticed as she folded his Levi's.

Romantic? More Like Masochist – Mary Dooty (she/her)

I am a hopeless romantic, I see love where there is none.
I let the needle prick my skin just so I could watch the rosy color and embrace the pain,
The feeling,
I would let you destroy me, only I am better whole.
If you could see the inside of my heart, it is torn from the inside out.
I write love poetry in my flesh, carved with Cupid's arrows.
Only it is not the romance I am seduced by,
I am pleasured by the endorphins that release in my brain.
Red is the color of romance, but it is also the color of blood, of pain and heartbreak.
Ripping out my heart and displaying it for the world to see.
I am obsessed with the feelings, the emotions.
There is the selfish need to know myself,
To familiarize every nook and cranny.
I shatter my heart only to stitch it back together again the next day.
I am a moth and tears are the flame I am drawn to.

Untitled: – Ant (they/them)

put your thumb in the crease
pull it down with your might
the orange knows how to
persist.

but if you don't peel it
it'll glow into your skin
replace what's already
there.

do you see the slice that
falls away first
pretend that's the last
time you'll ever be
unhappy.

and eat it with your hungry
teeth, seeds and all.

A chessboard, A match – Ant (they/them)

a chessboard,

a knight moves
tedhi chaal, you say

i am 4 years old,
and don't yet know
what it means to
live. or what it
means to feel fear.
i don't yet know
that it's the same
thing.

a pawn moves,
seedhi chaal, you say.
you are 10 years old,
and do not believe
that this house is
everything you could
have. you think you
are trapped. you don't
yet know that there is
no difference.

the queen moves,
you don't have
anything to say.

we are 18 and 24
i dream, sometimes,
of seeing mississippi
swell under my
fingertips. you dream
sometimes, of tasting
lyon.

we are 18 and 24.
we watch tv together,
sometimes. we think
this is all there is.

All My Tragedies Are Friends – Alice Carroll (she/her)

I know, I know, I know. Really.

Even friendship might not be sustainable

But then we were talking over each other

Because there's not a rift in any timeline

Where you can muffle your spontaneous laughter at what I was trying to say

And how terribly I said it

You loved me for what I meant to say

And even in spite of it

Somehow, I still want to know everything

Even if it only brings you relief

Because that vacancy cradles empty air

And you were speaking to me

Like an old friend and a perfect stranger

There – Christian Ryan Ram Malli (he/him)

You gave me a country.

                    I gave you

                    the summer

I prayed

for maggots.
intention

                    There was never an

between teeth that was

                    tender enough

                    to pray for.

I pinch

a sky
empty,

                    and look at my hands, how

how full of sky,

                    how the sky

                    turned out to be

one big lie.
You,

                    full of age

and memory of algae.

                    My mother,

                    a sliver

of your only love.

You reach   for her thigh and she

disappears into a month   you won't
                                       be found.

Porcelain

silence   and its subsequent shatter,

streets you won't   have a name for,
                                       nor sound.

And what are you

left with   but a pulsing place.

Somewhere, the slow fact   of death
                                       finds your voice,

and then your face.

And then,   my face,

which is to say   look, a car, look
                                       something standing

without the genius of bedrock,

look, a summer   with all the maggots

that have not happened.   Look at that boy
                                  with dreams

made of earth. Look
at him wake up   in it, inconsolably solid.

Look where I look,   look without feathers;
                                  the roof needs fixing,

the faucet leaks,
the quiet needs fixing   and leaks.

When It All Ends Georgina Will Never Know – Christian Ryan Ram Malli (he/him)

I.
I call my dick Georgina. Pronouns are she/her.
No deep history or whatever really. At least
not one I actively conceived. In the intersection
of sleep, there is a grogginess where a fissure rives.
The floor is not floor but hands, and Georgina
is somewhere made of touch and cracked lip.
Every man who ever touched me looks the same.
They all look like touch.

II.
The fucker whose smile reminds me of a gash
tells me he's tired of Grindr. Had opened himself up
on pavements, had birds peck at his innards to check
if he can still open up for himself. *Aren't you?* he asks
as he tilts his face skyward. I nod but that's where
we met anyway, and I can only look at the birdless sky,
then at him. But not in a romantic way. Ew. I do it
because he is vanishing. Piece by piece. The birds
are finishing up and he is inside all of their bellies.

III.
A couple of months before that, a lover
tells me I need to stop getting lost.
Meaning, names should be inserted with pressure
until the mind is able to categorize. Okay,
that lamppost is the sign I should go ask somebody
for help, and this is the part my vision betrays logic,
and I feel like I'm flesh on top of flesh,
never the final flesh and that drives me crazy.
Georgina doesn't have the same problem.
Perks of being a dick. Whenever I get lost,
I would open Grindr, and Georgina,
is of course, happy. That makes one of us.

IV.
Years from now I will grieve a name I have not met.
Someday, I won't meet anybody at all, and the birds
will come like rain. And when I say that, I mean
they won't cease to be until the gods forgive me.
Or Georgina. But she won't give a fuck since she's a dick.
And she won't bloom like she used to. She won't notice.

& – Christian Ryan Ram Malli (he/him)

I cut you as you advised me to & I cut you like a story &

  I cut you the way I would a line

when an idea halts &   it becomes an eternity inside me &

  lachrymose, I go out &

someone spits the word end & it doesn't make sense anywhere in our city

  where end is always succeeded by &

soon, a new September & you will have travelled so far &

  I remember the face you wore,

flashing in the crowd & stream & we usually met at nighttime & once

  we didn't & as I stared at your misplaced

stride in daylight, I thought & despaired: the moon was rising

  in the living room instead of the horizon &

I talked & talked with you like I always did & a man

  is nothing but sensation with the lights off &

something liminal prods my arm & you were there for so many mornings &

  I told my father about you &

he held me like the ocean & that means he cried &

  always, he said, I'm slipping away &

I know you hate fathers & their blunt ends & I hate dogs &

  I told you that & with mischief

you asked: what if I want us to get a horse? & I shrugged &

  just how many years did that promise you &

now, in the gaiety of the day I expect the moon & its startling

  skin & my silence has become a unique way

126

to say your name & I cut you   like the discussions we had

        about dreams & not necessarily a dream

but what you thought of them &   their primal sources & you

        used to cut a portion of my day &

made me realize that dreams   are as real as blade & I can't stop &

        the meaning of dreams should be tedious &

what verbiage & scene &   what came after astrology & myth &

        I need you to tell me what is after this &

The women in my family have long memories – Amy Devine
(she/her)

It is 1975 and she is learning to grieve, cracked teacups and stained
saucers filter into her thoughts like oil slicks
It is 1963 and she is dancing for the last time in years. She breaks
heels and promises.
It is 2022 and she is taking her first breath. Her stormcloud eyes
open into wonder, her impossible hands grip the air, and they ask
themselves if she will grow up to prefer tulips or sunflowers.
It is 1984 and she is crouched on the roof outside her bedroom
window. She dances calloused fingers over scar tissue and thinks
about how she will never be seen again.
It is 2009 and she falls in love.
It is 1959 and she chooses the wrong man but the right future.
It is 1947 and she argues with her mother over a thrown shoe, a
dropped 'haitch'.
It is 1986 and she is being handed a tragedy through the phone. She
slides down the wall and thinks of teacups.
It is 2018 and she is dancing in heather.
For the first time.

Expectations vs. Reality – Amy Devine (she/her)

Expectation: You have one body and that is enough
Reality: Some days the curve of your spine feels like tree roots, gnarled and pitted from rot
As you pad barefoot from room to room you can feel this chafe of your thighs and it reminds you that you are physical breath, you are tangible space within tangible space
Someone could reach out and scrape you from top to tail
Someone could fold you in on yourself, but you would not break
and, oh, how you long to be broken

Expectation: You can do anything you set your mind to
Reality: You had a fever five years ago and you fear that you never truly recovered
You feel it slipping between the thoughts that thawed, the unbidden and the boding

Expectation:
Reality: It is still too much

Of The Essence – Carla M. Cherry (she/her)

I be like
bedrock
undergirding
soil
sand
ocean floor.

Without me,
the roots of the
oak
sweet gum
sassafras
middlemist red
hydrangea
will not take hold,
leaves or blossoms unfold.

Let Charon and his skiff
hasten down the Styx!
I am
Ferrywoman of the living.

I be like
Calcium.
Bone-building.
Like actin and myosin,
motivating muscles,
striated and smooth.

Oh, but for
alembic you,

my
Magnesium,

how I could
metabolize,
coax
Vitamin D
calcitonin,
propel water into
plasma,
pabulum of blood into
The Four Chambers,
propagate into arteries,
vessels,
veins,
capillaries,
to and from the
brain
arms
neck
hands
hips
legs?

With every proceleusmatic
oeillade
I unfurl for you like
the Queen of the Night.

Perdure this
Fidelity,
fingers
legs
wrapped
around each other in
loving lattice

Seeds – Carla M. Cherry (she/her)

With red eyes
red ties
splitting white shirts down the middle
Proud Boys
waving flags
busting glass

no real stimulus in sight

Storm Wall Street
in this modern-day Jericho

Sow seeds of compassion

Plant sycamores
from Pennsylvania Avenue
to Park Avenue

The moneychangers,
the uber rich,
They build
skinny
super skyscrapers
Perch themselves
by their panoramic windows

Look down on the throngs:

workers, who can't pay their rent
the hungry queued up for boxes or plastic bags
of chicken and vegetables so they can eat this week,
the homeless,
their encampments swept away,
shuttled between hotels and
filthy shelters that rob their safety and dignity,

tenants who live with mold,
block holes in the walls with furniture,
leave food out so rats don't bite their babies

When the prophets come

command the moneychangers,
The 1%

to make haste

invite the prophets to abide in their houses,
and listen.
Give half their goods to the needy.

Let robber barons
pay on capital gains
with glad and giving hearts,
restore the masses fourfold.

And when the seeds of the sycamores fall
pick them up,
drop them into
median strips,
rat holes,
in front of office buildings,
golf courses,
mansions,
front yards and backyards.

Somebody,
plant a sycamore

Eve – Carole Greenfield (she/her)

Ascend the rungs of your ribcage,
God instructed us when we first learned
to breathe.

I try to climb slowly as panic gathers
but my breath snags on that rib
of his.

I don't believe I'll ever reach
my collarbones.

Do you think of leaving? he murmurs, holding me
on his lap, his lips warm along my jaw. I say nothing,
shake my head no. Where on earth would
I go?

At night while he sleeps beside me, mouth open,
I imagine removing that slender bone
beneath my breast, boring holes
at either end,

five more down one side,
putting it to my lips and walking out
past hedges, briar roses,
and the last tangle
of wisteria.

Not even God could name
this new sound,

the melody of lungs filling and falling,
only my own ribs around them.

Mother's Silk Dress – Elizabeth Kirkpatrick-Vrenios (she/her)

Everything she ever wanted is here
in this oblong cardboard box:
each blemish covered, painted red lips,
body smooth as butterfat,
curves covered with silk,
silence.

The orange poppies on the dress
Shrivel up and blister,
black crescent moons curl inward
in the flame, pressing their lips tight
against her thin smile,
against the sounds she makes
as she burns, black tongues
too vivid for her pale face.

On this special day of casseroles
stacked to the heavens,
her silver-blond hair blossoms
into a bonfire that licks
the ice-blue body.

Ravens flock to the window
wearing grief like black suits.
I long to fly with them
leaving this irreversible fire.

Raven (rā′vən) – Elizabeth Kirkpatrick-Vrenios (she/her)

Noun
1. (Zool.) (Corvus corax), similar to the crow, but larger, with a harsh, loud call. A traditional trickster hero among the native peoples of the Canadian Pacific Northwest.
2. A dark stranger come to town.
3. A pepper streak across the night sky.
4. Open beak, a room I cannot enter.
5. A sneer, a leer in a rough corvine heart.
6. A black, shiny color; when days are torn from their edges.
7. A scrap of paper flying over the cliff.

Adjective
1. Jet black; Star-crossed silhouette pressed against my mask.
2. Darkness; Only one third of the trees eaten by shadow.
3. Nuisance; such small cruelties in the empty house.
4. Impossible; double knot the end of every truth.

Verb transitive
1. Never a good idea to let your nightmares out.
2. Pokes a hole through a rookery of balloons
3. To obtain or seize by violence; Life does this, doesn't it?
4. To devour with great eagerness; We are fire or the image of it.
5. To tuck behind your ear a secret grief.
6. I pin my breath to his flight.

Verb intransitive
1. To seek or seize prey; Sometimes life finds one hole in the wire.
2. To be greedy; Only one third of the compost is eaten by lime.
3. To prowl for food; The itch of a match is fire.
4. Even salt tastes like sugar.
5. We all eventually become shadows.

Pain Like a Raven, Will Leave on That Last Note – Elizabeth Kirkpatrick-Vrenios (she/her)

while listening to Water Boy by Don Shirley
"Water boy, where are you hiding?"

my heart   a raven   an upside-down kite
on the Pacific headlands
          cries   on   the wind
soars   on   mournful notes
          carried to   the peak of a phrase
only to   that moves to the next   and the next
climbs   to the peak of the wave
          ripples   the   keyboard
my son's wings whipped by the wind,
          flutter   fail
oh water boy where are you hiding?

yellow poppies unwrap   their skirts
to a fat bumblebee   a cello
defies gravity   drunkenly   loops
from one   golden   cup   to another
each note not   like any other
this moment will never
come again
oh glorious water boy!

I am walking with love   and death
a familiar melody   a worn rut
that leads to the ocean

Getting Lost – Ed Ahern (he/him)

Alders and scrub weed,
once pushed through
yield to popple and firs,
crouched under moving in.
The crows and buzzards,
flies and wasps,
are left behind in sunlight,
but the mosquitos abide
and bedded down deer.
The hot breath of long grass
gives way to damp rot
splayed out in the bowels
of mature hickories and oaks.
There are no trails
nor anyone alongside,
nor sunlight allowing
guesses at direction.
Shapes without pattern
decayed aromas enveloping,
sounds muted into silence.
Gentle upwelling of fear
sharing me with delight.
A forest to which
I can't belong
but want to.

Your Kindness Is Startling – **Lucia Cherciu** (she/her)

Confirming joy:
once I weed around the pear tree
the squirrels find the fruit.

The symbiotic relationship
between apples and poison:
the stewardship of fruit trees

teaches about the futility
of dreams without pest control.
What use are the lavish meals

if that's the sentence
I remember?
Do you want to see

painted on the bus
what you say to your child
when you're tired?

Eloquence is a menace
to fragile grammar.
Envy trudges up the hill

obstinate like an ad about belly fat.
The truth doesn't always
quench the thirst.

Minerals – Nissa Valdez (she/her)

I am a motherless mother who sprang from a motherless mother,
but I remember these waters & being held by the amnion. Born
to mother & break the curse coursing through the female line.

Hot water springs up all along the Rio Grande. Plated minerals lie
in thick whitish deposits on concrete walls. Water seeps up through
rocks in the ground. The room smells of sulfur. Soles of my feet feel
heat rising.

My sons spent two hundred & sixty-six days gestating. Sixty-three of
them hooked to a steady drip of magnesium sulfate, slowing uterine
contractions in my strongest muscle. Begging back the quiescent
state of myometrium.

Concrete cell of my fifth-floor hospital room with an adjustable bed.
Peripheral venous catheter sticking into the back of my bony hand.
My view of the tall steeple of church a block away from our house
peeked over rooftops.

Two placentas laid like lily pads, tethered by umbilical cords
connecting them to me. Their mammalian formations in crucial
stages of development. I waited in gratitude of making it this far.
Eyes building millions of photoreceptors

& lungs taking their first watery practice breaths. Sometimes fear
came undone. I prayed, pleaded, cried—made deals I wasn't sure I
could make good on. Everything in me would try. I counted each
minute

towards fetal milestones. Tried not to pass the poison of trauma
through the cord. Instead, the knowing we were meant to be
together. Making our way with one another. Love holding us.

Always.

Of Water – Nissa Valdez (she/her)

Zealous faith in religion or medicine always seemed perilous. Now with
your pending diagnosis, could I? Could it help? It wasn't mononucleosis or
xanthoma. I grasped for support, prayed for goodness & mercy. We'd wait
weeks in this unknowing—but knowing you had cancer. Walking through
valleys of shadowing death, scenarios widening out before me, dread
unfurled—becoming a single mother—destitute, our two-year-old
twin sons growing up fatherless, your earthly constancy & steady strength
spent. How many more times will I walk into your loving arms &
rest my chin on the reassuring knob of your twice-broken clavicle?
Questions dissolved into disbelief, grief, anger. More tests, more
pain extracted. Bone marrow aspiration and biopsy—sound of cold metal—
objectionably forceful drilling—your sturdy iliac bone punctured—ghastly
needle drawing out your potent essence, core, sum & substance,
mined for analysis. We waited & I relived my lessons of purgatory.
Lymphoma—there are more than seventy different types. I dug for
knowledge, hoping that would save you, learning new medical
jargon & memorizing physiology to coax a cure. Lymphatic system, part of the
immune system, produces white blood cells, removes cellular debris,
helps maintain fluid balance. Suffix -oma: morbid growth or tumor. Lymph:
goddess of water or water. Nodes, vessels, ducts—moving, manufacturing,
filtering, absorbing, protecting. I moved from physical, tangible, to
ethereal—scraping meaning from each hallowed bit of time with you,
days stretched into weeks then stopped. Each second distinct, eternal.
Cancer carried time strangely—we were meant a lifetime together, resting
beside still waters, clinging to love, always. Realized—then—
absolved: illusion of control vanished.

Left hand it the world rolling – Valyntina Grenier (she/her)

The roar of waves curling towards the soft shore I going off a cliff
refract the cosign might of the harvest moon dress four early morn
the grinding stone/ flour/ coffee beans/ steam/ chatter/ rolling
back/ along track across a field razing reaping buying land growing
hot house plants planting roots my teeth ache anger and ink in
sleep each sweet-swell-sea-shell-crown-chakra-super-moon-
charged-crystal-oil *love it* Watch this calm catch the light high and
tight glint of palm Pollen pitched to the sky a hummingbird alights
before a searing last ray of *lethal aid* I squander/ ignite lite-death-
cult-capitalist-acid-calm night

Dress Our Souls – Valyntina Grenier (she/her)

Many unsure prisoners are held silent

Caged children wail
before our narrow/ cuffed/ alien-making law
The guards' sadistic lives
are painted as
un-planned knowledge

A desperate don't
stop
behind their gaze

Many gentle protestors sway
they stay
to sing a lullaby

Children fight sleep
under the guards' eyes chanting
Mamá

-

Many women dress our souls so
we flatten capitalism before more

mortals disappear as so many bills
flying against ourselves over eons of tools

Symbols medias run are awakening
to open fields of wonder

Women w/ our arrows
before cleared plots of grass

Grave sights floor alien peace

-

So, posts your running

many violent postings
out their symbol
air their impotent heart
reveal all "lovers" covered
Ignite your fears

Resign/ quit/ condemned

Only harken, for many arrows

-

Alien peace embraces our atheism w/ poems

We bow our awakening
Our narrow-placid law
is running hate w/ full coverage
Knowledge faked is dim

Time's up
Let's square up
all touch all
beaten bridges

-

You, all betting on your laurel
shoving your tongue in your cheek
you harken
your remonstrance
we reject as lies

And you all, resting on your haunches
lawmakers laid bare
lying under your god

all violence
we eject on sight

Inside exactly one second
step off the scale

Impossible-to-thrive-with-paper-rakes
don't throw the case Don't acquit
Mend

-

All prisoners without cause alien your gavel

We aren't all unsure prisoners

Unsure alien—all lovers
Unsure alien—all knowing
Unsure alien—all gentle

You from a gavel held up by law war-like band you harken

all evil isn't clothed so the circle of laws mounts the peace

Ninety-Nine Times Out of a Hundred – Howie Good (he/him)

Crime was somewhat common in those days, and the law itself often criminal. No one ever felt totally safe. Thousands perished in fires and car wrecks and from untreated medical conditions. When I complained of crippling back pain, the doctor said it was just my body attacking itself. That was what it was like to be a person in this world. The family dog howled and howled as if in protest. Meanwhile, the children exchanged conspiratorial glances around the dinner table, their eyes like burn holes.

&

Whether I'm screwing or just thinking, I'm regularly being interrupted—called to the phone, sent on a beer run, required in person at work. Everyone always seems surprised when I make it back home. And why wouldn't they? I've too often displayed on tennis courts or dance floors all the skill and grace of an inebriated kangaroo. Regardless, I receive a postcard in the mail guaranteeing me a chance to win one of 1,000 prizes. Me! A man who on a cloudless day holds a black umbrella over his head.

&

Have you ever been in the shower when there was an earthquake? Dated a relative by accident? Wanted to eat toothpaste? Ripped off your pants while dancing? Been unable to recognize your own reflection in the mirror or differentiate between faces and objects? It's like walking into a hallucination without being quite sure whose it is. I kind of wish Baudelaire was alive to see it. Under the turmoil of a cankerous sky, there's a fire made of people.

First World Problems – Howie Good (he/him)

They're auctioning off the unwashed and still stained underwear Elvis wore on stage beneath his iconic white jumpsuit. The darkness at the root of things inevitably seeps to the surface. I try ignoring my pathetic yearning for something better or at least different, but I can't, no more than I could a rooftop sniper firing randomly into a crowd I had joined. And it's not like I'm a guy committed to the dictionary definition of words. What they call progress, I would call cold impotent twilight.

Hometown Melodrama – Eric Abalajon (he//him)
After Ina Kapatid Anak (Lino Brocka, 1979)

Staring outside the window of a borrowed car, after   twenty
years
Pura goes home from America   to an unchanging hometown, the
mansion

where she grew up now surrounded by dust and dried grass.
Entering the house,
new faces are seen   on the ground floor   passing the time
            with gambling and gossip

like a slum community under one roof   made up of workers and
helpers sheltered
with former children   now carrying their own babies. The
welcoming party stayed

behind when Pura went up   the stairs. Not once do we hear her
bedridden father.
Emilia, the sister left behind teaches piano   while holding a
bottle of beer. The suspension of

the house both inside and out   in time is oddly haunting.
            Posturing as more knowledgeable, Pura wants to sell   the
art deco property, better if it's made into museum

before it truly falls apart   and this again ignited strife
            temporarily halted by distance
in a household   long ruined. The success of the outsider is
both admired and scorned,

in an unchanging hometown,   slaps thrown during the wake and
other eruptions
are resolved as soon as Pura leaves once more. What's going to
happen to the house now?
And to the people living on the first floor?

riding dark horse nightmare – Joan McNerney (she/her)

to prison library
where sewer
backs up flooding
cages of books
my brains are washed
by a short scientist

detectives trail me
arrested by police
giving up to
handcuffs ether

now on train
calendars peel
off cars
1942   1962   1982
2198   1892   1294
passengers screaming
screaming off track
burning 3rd rail

in swamp struggling
to reach green reeds
i   am   a
fixed target
paper duck
*pull trigger*fire pin*thru barrel*into muzzle*
b u l l e t   s h o t
paper duck
mowed down.

Lost Dream – Joan McNerney (she/her)

I am driving up a hill
without name on an
unnumbered highway.

This road transforms into
a snake winding around
coiled on hair pin turns.

At the bottom of the incline
lies a dark village strangely
hushed with secrets.

How black it is. How difficult
to find that dream street
which I must discover.

Exactly what I will explore
is unsure. Where I will find it
is unknown. All is in question.

I continue to haunt gloomy
streets in this dream town
crossing dim intersections.

Everything has become a maze
where one line leads to another
dead ends become beginnings.

Deciding to abandon my search,
I return for my automobile...
nowhere to be found in shadows.

Finally I look up at the moon's
yellow eye...my lips forming
prayers to a disinterested god.

Three-Headed Hippocampe – Émilie Galindo (she/her)

Beyond double-doors—*zzzzz sore from zonked out urchin knobs*
There's a back room, black room
moved one stairwell down. Same building, same floor.
with padded message-in-a-VHS walls

A fishing net dangles from the ceiling—*collected or caught seashells*
Bring one to your ear and listen for
The three-headed *hippocampe's* wail
—Like butter on a tin can wound—

The first head has an anise-steeped cigarette stuck to its lower lip
It barks, like a toothless moped, highballing obscenities at its razor-
gnawing and Armageddon-chewed wife &
at its stoned-pea-and-starched-pear-in-a-pod daughters
One rides the grass while the other rides the beach worms

Crane over the net to spot Cerenity—*the fog dissipating goldfinch*
But it's more jellyfish pellets & kelp ruminations
Puffed up by the empty tortoise shell pegged to the black ceiling
Loving requires toilet paper—*to wipe the ashes off the toilet seat*

The second head's got grass stretched eyes & a crabby underbite
Asbestos mottled moans zing out of its mouth
Building bisque sandcastles, periwinkle stairwells
Yet leaving the secondhand razor-shells & barks
already edited for the third head to reclaim, hold.

The three-headed *hippocampe* riffs on its 3-stringed wound
Estranged strings, their moans ring out one by one
Domino strings, *ré mi fa mi fa mi*
Fa wobbles, picked like scab, hoping for no *sol*

The third head, shaggy hemp hair & pearl eyes,
sings of sideways scars & of the subsiding symmetry that
doesn't quite swallow the sandcastles,

nor solves the sludge riddles & bundles in the cellar,
still, it stirs the salt & the cinnamon & brings about Cerenity

In the back room, the black room
memories are bottled up in muscle-shelled VHS
& serenaded by a three-headed Hippocampe
it's all behind—*light rings out of the urchins' coffee breath*

A Brain Freeze, Coppers & Squares – Émilie Galindo (she/her)

Ash is sitting on the kitchen floor.
Facing the fridge.
Curled up. Folded up.
Legs folded up against his chest
his veiled brow, green bandana, is resting against his knees,
looking in
& enclosed by his arms. Squared.

The flickering clang of copper hooded eyes scalds the nape of his
neck scarlet.
Their copper hooded eyes. Arrow slits.
He, their once crisp, now jilted, ticket to nowhere.
Glass pins keel over with a stained t-shirt sigh.
Robed up against the arrow slits. The copper hooded eyes.
Swaddled in a comfort that's really a noose around his neck.
Around his neck.
Around his neck.
Around his neck.
GASPS.

Ash uncurls & unfolds
Ash is sitting up. Sitting back. Palms against the cold tiles.
Sweat darkens the emerald green of his bandana & buffets the
paisley patterns.
He crawls to the fridge and opens it
the cold goes SPLASH against his red & swollen face.
He finds in front of him a barrier of Heineken bottles
he grabs one
but before he has the time to do anything
the lid goes POP and a tiny spider crab crawls out of the bottle and
back into the fridge
where Ash's mum is setting the table.
Unfazed.
She doesn't see him

her not-yet-copper-hooded eyes are laser focused on the octopus
on the silver platter garnished with red corals.
The octopus extends one of its tentacles
and wraps it around Ash's waist,
like the rope of the robe,
and brings him in. Sets him on the cool platter.
He can't breathe under water. The red corals bleed copiously.
A retractable pen swims by. Clicking. Or possibly tutting.
Er. Why, what the fuck are you doing in there?
An iridescent & shimmering Gab approaches.
She takes his hands and pulls him out.
Dude, you know the drill, never alone. Never!

Next he's sitting on a bean bag, on the patio.
I'm gonna get you a cuppa coffee.

Ash stares out into the garden
Flatly black yet patterned. Shimmering. Like an optical illusion.

You okay, mate?
The out of the blue voice jars Ash
Ash looks left, where the voice is.
Former temp worker turned hip manager in a young startup
company that specialises in turning rubbish into pricey furniture.
The man is square-shouldered and hipster-dressed. Ash is especially
intrigued by his green silk vest, worn over a black t-shirt. Ash
imagines the man standing beside him, currently sipping his brown
drink through a metal straw, preening like a peacock in front of his
mirror before coming to the party.
Why are you acting like we're friends?'
No tottering. No trudging. They crawl sideways. Pinch sharply.
Ain't we?
Ash sees a Gillette ad in his beard & the copper sheen of his ringed
fingers.
You're such a fucking phoney poser, man.
I had no idea you're a mean drunk.

Your beard is a fucking magpie nest of shiny shit. You drink beer out of a fucking crystal pint. Fancy fuck.
Silence. The browbeaten man is hurt. Ash finally infers that the green of his vest is not peacock, but mallard.
You're just fucking bitter, mate. You're stuck between a rock and your own bullshit, so don't take it out on me.
He splits.
Gab is back with the coffee.
Ash stirs the sugar in. And licks the sweet silvery spoon.
Where do ducks go?

320: Paper Blades – Émilie Galindo (she/her)

Sssss.

Sibilant heat was printing on sour faces.

Twirling pens were at once slashing the air

and fanning our scarlet smacked mugs.

We were zealously gnawing the fleshy words on our tongues.

Last names were frostily laid down on pages.

Blunt ballpoint pens bled the liability out of affiliation.

The table, which splintered, pricked our bear forearms,

was dotted with silver paper clips.

But it's the sly stapler that got to sink its teeth in the paper.

Unconditional had been renegotiated down

to 50 from the family and 320 from the *région*.

Cause blood isn't binding.

Clicking and whirring

were the grating preamble

to the rescue from the flesh.

Monochromatic characters drafted for conciliation.

-

A dash stipulated Family therapy.

Which was to be annulled on account of anamorphosis.

6 eyes to 2. the chair drooped under the weight of my ears.

Well...not quite. 2 eyes had fallen. Wedged in the furrows of the wooden floor.

I got up. As erect as the I in flight. *End of simile.*

They were renouncing *me. I* was renouncing screaming into my skull.

The mitigator's thumbtack eyes tried to pin me to my chair.

'I can't do this, go home alone, and survive.' Dripped out.

-

They had already washed their hands of me

in the black ink that delimited & sustained my life.

No love, no 50 to spare.

Just the black ink.

An adoptive covenant kindly substituting for a tacit agreement.

Black ink. Practical. Impartial. Protective.

Protection had gotten snagged on the barbed wire of our family's nest.

Still, that's what it all was. A poorly executed exercise in protection

-

Should I be thankful?

Acknowledge: *self-awareness, contingencies, opportunity, second chances.*

But, then again, to me, a grapefruit tastes better when bitter.

Look, with my 2 eyes,

out the anamorphic contraption.

At very least, bedeck the black letters

with garlands of nuances.

To tip the printed words away

from resentful.

Burning bridges – Sana Mujtaba (she/her)

And again, the words take me back to the chasm that would never
be filled without you in the scene
And the one that can be saved is sleeping under the ribcage,
palpitating occasionally
Erratic microseconds run behind doors
Old newspapers and VHS are glad to remain intact and abandoned
They carry the pride of bonafide past
Psychedelic grief sits deep within the spine of the bookshelves, and
the potpourri is stale because too many regrets are mixed with
essential oils

Jasmine perfume-filled hair braided neatly to hide the unscathed
paranoia
The resplendent aura smoldering the pacts between two skies
And the petrichor of eastern soil is adamant to hold the rotten roots

Kiss my wrists and pour the void into my soul
Make a pincushion out of my heart
As the nascent sorrows hang from the eyelids
The need for endless reassurance is turning the waves back to shore
As tears are not allowed to roll down the aging cheeks
Imprisoned behind stones, the tears will rest on the revolting
junctions
Someone is walking faster around the lulled clouds
Like a thunderclap, the words will knock on the doors
And Icarus will burn again in a foreign inferno

my choice – Dana Kinsey (she/her)
a Golden Shovel after Gwendolyn Brooks

a woman is either petrified or jubilant if

she's pregnant. You should know I

once poisoned

my thinking with the

notion that definite endings are easier than difficult beginnings.

Voices I clung to spoke of

your biological classification, your impossibility, reasons your

body (though poppyseed-small) should never know the breaths

that exhale to word and song and kiss. I

try (every day) to believe

that

as I dragged myself to the clinic and even

as I dared to arrange letters that could name you in

the turquoise sequined notebook stashed in my

nightstand, my deliberateness

was not crime or sin. I

(fancied you a rapture like dayspring or stardust and so) was

never, not

ever, going to use my pen to end your story (so dreamlike & deliberate)

Goddess Complex – Jodie Oakes (she/her)

Another bastard
Catholic boy
Come here
And mess up
My pretty face

Your palm cracks like paper
Against my cheek

Your saliva is gunmetal
I think I may drown
But who wants to die
On polyester sheets

A butcher scent
Fills the room
Clinging to that stack
Of Nietzsche paperbacks

Planted like a flag
Beside your bed

Yes, God is dead
And I want to be violent
And violated
I want you to remember

That you did
Terrible things

I can tell you have
A goddess complex
You pray at the altar
First light, grey milk

Open your mouth
Open your mouth

This bed is where
Your old self
Comes to die
Your hands, an axe

No one can laugh
At the girl who will split /
spit on your face

Even if you leave me
I still spat
In your face

Dirty Magic – Jodie Oakes (she/her)

I dream of you three times
Even though Bonnie says
I shouldn't play with dirty magic.

In a fit of languid spring madness
I rub my wrist on the inside collar
Of the coat you left behind.

I think if I show my face
For seven days straight
I will become unforgettable.

I'm trying to make a feast of my famine
Where every crumb gets cut
With the finest silver

The flash of a blade
Bearing down
on something sinuous.

In my stomach
A poison walnut husk
Spikes the fat full moon
Of childish desire.

I take my blood magic to town,
Driving fast past sunflowers
Broken and bowed.

Listening to angry music
Made by all the blond and bony boys
Who never loved me.

What's one more for the list.

We sit in the May sun
Perched above the city
Like pegs on a clothesline

I'm only hanging myself out to dry.

I answer questions never asked
And grab every static crackle of electricity
From an overarching sky

That's clearly trying too hard.

I want something to shatter my bones
Break me in a different way
I'm tired of telling the story

Of the day you sold your blood
To buy a silver ring
That cut off my own supply
I guess you always thought
I was smaller than I am

Let me drown in suede and saltwater
We are all dead anyway

We are all beautifully

Alive

First Time – Jodie Oakes (she/her)

He sketched a bird on your arm
Until you felt faint
And had to dig your heels in
Warm linoleum.
A baby crying in the other room.
It's just a cat scratch he said
As the light glugged in
Lazy with dust motes
And stale cigarette smoke
From his wife's *Marilyn's.*
I had a dream
You told him,
That I got shot—
It was heavy in my guts
And the only time
I felt truly alive.
There's sex in death.
He digs the needle in
Until the bird begins to bleed
What about now
He asks.
The sea calls us home
It says
moreto ni zove u doma
Sea speaks home.
Of course,
Instead of all that
We sit in silence
The walls close in
With the heat of summer
Sharp objects
And atoms eating space,
Leftover particles
Of places past.
But there really is a baby

Crying in the other room.

Your husband picked you up
To fuck in the back of a van
In a corn field dressed for
Golden slumber.
He grabbed your naked arm
And didn't say much
He may have put a ring on your finger
But the other boy burnt a bird
Into living flesh.
He could roll over you like an ocean
Salty and slick
Calling you home.
But instead
He takes your tongue
And drowns it

Rage – April Renee (she/her)

i felt her there, though i did not let the
fumes slip between the gaps in my teeth
my throat always smelled of loss
quiet, unattended to
i had a heart too soft to scream
too soft to ever be hard, but now
i have lost the stillness
of my childhood
the smell of tearstained books
and lamps left burning until morning
i have begun to reek of
a rotting rage
left too long in the sun
i must have forgotten her
must have been too desperate
to escape the heat
abandoned the thing i didn't have the energy to carry
pretended the smell wouldn't catch up to me
left her to become sharp & lonely
spiteful, even
wrecking the house
and demanding someone else clean up the mess
tonight, i hold her close
i wrap my rage in my favorite blanket &
read her poems that i haven't read since i was too young to
understand what they meant
her wet eyelashes find her sticky cheeks
finally, she rests
a window opens
not a sound is made

Portrait of a Bad Girl Gone Good – April Renee (she/her)

she used to be the type never to turn down a jello shot. now she is a housewife who only smokes when her husband is out of town. his demure sweetheart, she swallows her manicured nails and lets her belly fill with blood as his fingers land like a murder of crows on the skin of a mistress somewhere across the country. she once was a bar fly with potential. now that she has what she thought she wanted, she is left craving a drink. she never thought all the good times would be spent wondering if they are bad for each other. when he comes home he will claim amnesia of the fight they had before he left, and she will leave the silverware sticky in the sink as an act of protest. this is not the revolution she had dreamed of participating in. later, she will stare at her fractured reflection in the kitchen window and wash the dishes in defeat. remember that she is not a freedom fighter. she is the furthest thing from free.

I'M GROSS AND YOU'RE WELCOME – April Renee (she/her)

smoker's cough with a snappy mouth, i am exactly what your mother shouldn't want for you. i don't brush my teeth every day because my illnesses bind me to the bed like a hostage. i'm a collector of grippy socks and grudges, two days from the shakes. i forgot to refill my prescription today. when i run out of those slickly coated purple tabs, those chalky blue hail mary's, i will say things i don't mean. my under eyes are stained amaranthine and sometimes i pass out on the floor when i drink. i am the opposite of her, the girl you used to hold. she is rich, regal, refined. i am white trash and i think you like that about me. there's something to be said for my upbringing, as crude as it might be. i knock used shoes down from the telephone lines because why waste a perfectly functional item of clothing? all of my belongings are found on the street. i pee behind bushes, have sex on my period, and caress my own breasts. i mean, if i was just like her, how boring would that be?

Adult Chat – Sarah Henry (she/her)

To the man on the line,

it was a pressing matter.

He wanted to know

the size of my feet.

What was the length

and width?

He needed to hear

the truth. So far,

it was only speculation.

He guessed my right foot

held some appeal,

but the left

had its moments.

If he favored one,

the other would be jealous.

How was my circulation?

Good?

He wanted to handle

and fondle my feet,

just so. Did I find

this subject ticklish?

Were my arches fallen?

I might be wearing clogs

or sandals, with a bracelet

around my ankle,

like his.

After four hundred

and sixteen days

on arrest,

he was going to leave

his house to vacation

in the Blue Ridge.

Virginia is for lovers.

The mountain scenery

would look romantic

in the spring.

Did I care to join

him for a peep?

for when you leave – Louise Kim (they/she)

the tote-bag-toting baby gays
will all eventually learn to grapple with
the sting and punch of heartbreak.

well, that day isn't today
for me, and i'm indeed toting a tote bag
barely anything in it
i'm still standing as you leave the station
on the bullet train.

i'm still standing, looking at you, as you leave.

you're sitting, speeding away, looking
away from the window,
calling a friend
whose name i can't seem to remember.

as i walk back to ~~our~~ my apartment,
there on the street:
a sad, sad airpod dropped, forgotten,
in the snow.
a temporary exhale.

i now know that your parting
gift was an excerpt from didion's
"goodbye to all that" the part about her
leaving. so, then, goodbye
to all that.

first published in Work In Progress Magazine

and, i fear, ephemeral... – Louise Kim (they/she)

your fingerprints are fading away.
it's been a while since we were created,
perhaps essence preceding existence,
perhaps vice versa,
but one thing is for certain:
we were children of gods
and we will not last as long.

aging, us two.
this is a shell, and it is mortal.
this is a shell and i picked it
up at the beach last week,
the white sand slipping in between
the wrinkles of my fingers.

we were priestesses
living by feeling, living
virginally, by which i mean
we would not let gods sully us,
we believed we could live
untouched by the gods.
i won't pass any judgment
on our youthful selves.

sometimes we would
sit under the shade of the
willow trees near the pond—
the pond near your aunt's—
and wonder
why we were born,
why we were living.
what is being and
what is time.
do you remember?

and every autumnal equinox
it rained when we were together.
and we danced and sang,
momentarily renewed by
the rain
and all the fruit it bears.
the rain is eternal.
the rain never forgets.

your memories are fading away.

and i find myself sometimes,
sitting on our wooden chair,
looking out the window, muttering,
if only we were younger.
if only we were younger.

first published in The WEIGHT Journal

contemplating – Louise Kim (they/she)

i, dehydrated, soft-skinned,
always wishing for more than what is
always regretting more than what was

those moments in constant search
of the self and of the other and
the flux the boundaries the altitudes of the two

earth-shattering numbness returns again
i'd like to hold my heart in my palms
cradle it with care once it leaps out of my ribcage

baby's first steps
daring adventure into the unknown
i wonder what bravery is like

see me in the mundane
see my stain
look at me, staining everything

look around, all stained by me
my blood, my tears, my clipped fingernails and teeth
that fall out in moments of heartburn

from a tender age i
embodied a question mark
i just didn't know how sustaining

self-imposed sadness
or God-granted grief?
in either case, a tour de force.

A Wound Burns Like [Woman]. – Lev Verlaine (he/him)

The dream escapes me
into the no-open-air kitchen.
The porch is croaking standstill dreaming a way underneath.
     My home and my rest.
 If my room were abandoned, I'd still be in it.

The world's ending in ways you'd never imagine

        But you're still young, it's not in your hands, on your
shoulders.

In the outside earth
day bugs chatter.   Summer knows the end,
     tired of breaking rings over the doorway
    grasping for thousand dollars teeth on the high shelf.

I just need to tell myself. *I just need to tell myself.*
Maybe bad things don't need to happen to me.

I wake myself up and talk myself down
from the ledge I was born on.   I am still trying to desire.

stone-touched lover - Marianna Pizzini Mankle (she/her)

cobblestone streets and   crunch-cragged leaves in hues
          of red and brown: my only audience when I first
          fell in love.
I ran lotion-softened fingertips down
                              age-old brick and found
                              love was deeper than
                              I knew.
I lost my heart   to a rough-and-ready shell;
brown-toned brownstones with histories
all their own.   I blamed my stumbling
          steps on the uneven streets,
          but really I was just
overcome by the stories of my
                              newest lover: bell-toned warnings,
                              red-dusted steps, and
                              seas held at bay.

Culture of Transience – Sanket Mhatre (he/him)

It took a river for civilizations to be born
How else do you explain the nature of blood in our veins?

Rivers wait for none, sometimes, not even themselves
And here we are stuck in the make believe of eternality

Created to throw us off the scent of water
Too precious, like truth, residing in our atoms

Anything that doesn't change our body can never change us:
A law that stays hidden in deep trenches of our epidermis

Underneath all permanence lies everything in passing
Oceans, forests, islands, farms, clouds, cities—landmasses of desire

Suspended raft-like, floating on the ever-flowing waters of time
while we are left to determine our own culture of transience

The Simmered Sea – Daniel Moreschi (he/him)

Although the sea is pulled by lunar reins,
Its servile ebbs conceal the subtle strides
Of a fateful force, once nature's patience wanes,
To test its tether with unruly tides.

Where frozen hills are stoked by metal fumes
It brings a rhythmic ruse of turbulent grace
As thriving swirls are topped by sprightly spumes
That lead a charge, where growing flows retrace.

And while humanity ignores the signs
Of ominous plights—as billows belch and roar—
A steep caress erodes the coastal lines
And razes borders, like a siege of war.

A rising of tsunamis stirs the straits
Once swells attain the sways of ancient scales
And wayward spans cascade at mankind's gates
Where a ceaseless reach of simmered spite prevails.

When swept-up crowds are pleading for an ark
And lands are swallowed by the famished surge,
The moonlit sanctuaries turn to dark
For undulating chains of Gaia's purge.

179

L'Envois – John Barr (he/him)

Spiders aren't the only things to swing
from silk. Their moment come, the green
half-inches of inchworms dangles everywhere.

They lower of themselves like diving
bells, each fitted out and self-contained
for travels in the perpendicular.

But the green prodigious lowering
must also be in common comprehension
of a destiny they share.

Whatever home is to a driven thing,
they're not there yet but in the in-between,
the neither here nor there.

Some will ascend their silkenism, gaining
again the leaf whereon they eat and spin
and rise like angels to the nth power.

And some will not, falling
prey to the pattern and design
of Heaven-sent grub, forest fare.

God of the Shine, the Brought-Up Boy,
Author of Reverses and Comeuppance,
will your agents rise like booms from below
or will the danglers make it home?
Zero-sum but not a game,
you answer Yes. Yes. Yes.

Body Mine – Rye Owen (they/them)

What is this body of mine,
As I look upon it, I recognize it as such
Yet when I walk away from the reflective gaze
I recognize it not

These breasts which lay upon my chest,
will they stay forever?
For they betray my true nature

This stomach which rests upon my front,
will it last forever?
For it betrays my heart

This body mine,
How you toy with my heartstrings
You romance me with Renaissance artistry
Then you turn to betray me in fear and shame

This body mine,
How your shape betrays me
I look upon the others of this world and long for such
The curves of my side have no place in androgyny.

This body I wish to dispose,
Yet it stays connected to my very being
How I hate it.

I was Raised in Fear – Rye Owen (they/them)

I was born with the knowledge that breasts and curves and a feminine face was that of a target. Never walk home in the dark on your own. So, I walk home in the dark on my own, palming the cool metal of the rod shaped to my fingers, shaped to a point to pierce an attacker. I walk home knowing that while I am not a woman, I still feel the fear of one.

Exodus Across the Borderline – Nweke Benard Okechukwu (he/him)

the flight douses the pains of exiting a hometown where dust buries
   our placenta. & upon landing Bamako,
the streetlights ushered us in somewhere
   the government fixes variegated fingers of light.

at once, i slipped into the borderline of two
   tongues. because where a language ends,
another begins & struggles to cohabit.
   i hate myself, the first time to deny my

dialect to learn new intonation as if survival
   depends on eloquence. somewhere next
the hilltop, the air partying the birds eastward
   sameness my home glories their songs—

a reminder that sweetness exists everywhere
   as much as bitterness anywhere.
here, everything with a price tag.
   that to own air, you must break into

whatever can fly in space, say confetti.
   look, nowhere the bus drops off to pick
mint of the franc. this means nothing
   transforms except what you grip

into a desirable shape. like lighting a candle
   at night. see how i cut open myself a crescent orange
to bloom in a new country.
   like waters, it flows in me & everything

new, including my body.
   so, where there's no music, make a guitar.

Red Maple Flowers – Caitlin Gemmell (she/her)

These delicate fire seeds came to me today.
Each one a promise, an offer
to guard me from harm.
Or perhaps they're meant to rekindle the flames of my heart.

No matter their purpose, I tucked each red jewel
into the liminal pocket of my fuzzy,
grey cardigan, my fingers
gravitating towards them, feeling their satisfying,
diverse textures.

Then I sauntered home to potter about
arranging the fire seeds in patterns
as if arriving at the exact array
would somehow cause magic to blossom instantaneously.

The Soul of a Crow – Caitlin Gemmell (she/her)

The wind sings a farewell to summer song, encouraging the land wights to return to their beds in the moss. Do you hear it too? When did August become the first days of Fall? Was it always this way and I was too absorbed in other things to breathe in rhythm with the Earth's song?

The crow hears and answers in an endearing croak that hides a song every bit as melodic as the wind's gentle lullaby.

I hear your spirit song, dear crow. Sometimes I think you sing for me alone.

Twas a Nation – Hayden Kasal-Barsky (she/her)

Twas a nation without fear, covered in wounds
From big, loud bangs.
A tear dropped from the sky in June
And covered the land in doom.
This leak swam into our homes
Like a broken faucet
And shaped power into a fetus.
This was the new new we had to engrave into history
Twas a nation newly born to fear.

Duct – Stephanie Parent (she/her)

Duct tape is for fixing,
patching tears, hiding holes.
You can keep air from escaping an
inner tube, water from leaking out
a hose—

Make things work
a little

longer.

Draw out
the expiration

date.

He put duct tape over my lips,
play-acting one of those old detective
movies we both loved. He was the villain
capturing me, the damsel in distress,
pinning my hands above my head.
His mouth touched storm-shaded
polyethylene, and on the other side,
mine.

I could not taste the bitterness behind
his tongue, the way I had the previous day,
a new aversion I could not hide. With the
tape to keep me safe, I did not
turn away.

The pressure of his lips felt like
love from a distance. I remembered a time
when we did not need patching up, when
I needed no binds beyond my mind,

my heart.

Breathing plastic and rubber, smelling sweat
and cologne, I found peace. I let myself forget
what happens when you leave duct tape
on too long.

His hands/
          my lips

the rip/
          the rupture

the burn

      of a betrayal

      the betrayal

of a burn.

Words I Can Hear with My Skin – Carella Keil (she/her)

Falling out windows
climbing down
staircases with my eyes closed
Knowing
there is no bottom
this is the
bottom

I wish
you would yank the hair from my face
punch me in the eyes

Kiss me until my lips bleed, dig
into me, I want
to find my truth

Beneath your fingernails

Pound my breath and eyelashes
into the pillowcase
leave no room
for me to cry Out

When I was a child he said, never
look at the sun
it will blind you
so I covered my eyes, but now
I'm just as blind

He read to me
upside down and backwards
Now words don't make any sense.
I think you're beautiful
if you were older, I'd marry you

Dig out
the things I can't hide from
No.
you're wrong.
I can hide forever.

Live in my backroom apartment
with a can-opener and rusty spoons
a faucet that never stops dripping
moldy linoleum tiles
curling away from my feet

Don't stand here.

My walls caving with the weight
of old photographs
My hair twisted in knots, my face dirty with lies

bad dreams and screams stuck between
yellowing teeth
nowhere to escape from

Nowhere to escape to

At sunrise and sunset
My eyes are open windows for strangers to climb into.

I have too much empty space around my heart.

Throw away the keys I fought to hold
You know I'll only lock myself inside again
Kick in the walls, nail all my shadows
to a loose floorboard beneath the rug
step on all the sidewalk cracks
trace every line on my palm
draw some new ones

Break everything that isn't broken
until it's all
broken
and then I'll feel
w hole.

Don't dare
ever kiss
me goodbye.

I need words
I can hear with my skin.

I want to be the ocean

beneath a rising moon
I want a summer day
that never ends
I want

A sky that has no corners
all pages
bending to a moment

I want
This moment.

Alice and the Big Bad Wolf – Carella Keil (she/her)

Time is broken on my wrist
I spoke to Alice last night
She says she's been chasing rabbits

I ran through a field of white, white roses
Painted red. Thorns through my ankles
Wet dirt beneath my toes
Your bites still fresh on my neck

Sharp starlight broke beneath my feet
The moon grinned its Cheshire smile and
Bit me with jagged teeth

Scratch me, scratch me deeper
We're painting the roses red

Time is broken on the wall

I ran through a field of roses
Into a room of hardwood floors and candles
Burning on a tall, tall table, Burning

In a room with no corners and
Walls for windows
A four-poster bed and
Cracks on the ceiling growing like vines

You lie naked like a King in your bed

The first time we met I was ten times taller than you
I had blood on my lips
And a taste for wild boys
I pinned you to the mattress
My green eyes like daggers
And took what I wanted And took

What I thought I needed

Ten times later and I'm ten times smaller while you're ten times
    taller

Your room smells like rotted flowers

You say

Eat Me
Touch Me
Suck Me
Fuck Me

I hesitate, turn to the door
The door grows smaller and smaller each second I stare
I'm smaller and smaller each second I stay
Trapped like a rabbit with its foot in the snare
And so like a good girl I obey

Scratch me, scratch me deeper
We're painting the roses red

I spoke to Alice last night
She says it's a long way to fall
Down a rabbit hole

There's a key on the nightstand and
My tears on your chest
There's a clock on the wall and
Stale petals in your bed

Memories sift down on me like a pack of falling cards
I am your Whore of Hearts
Let's shuffle. Let's reshuffle again
Sex on the hardwood floor

There are cracks in the floor and cracks in a mirror
I am broken
Running on a pavement of crushed roses
Playing Grown-Up games

The girl in the looking glass is not me. She's Not Me.

There's a key in the mirror on the nightstand
And a girl in a pack of cards
Snubbed-out cigarettes, a roach, a wineglass, and melted candles
With black wicks
And Alice chasing rabbits

She says, You'd better change your lock, Girl
Stop letting the Jabberwocky in.

Tornado Season – Carella Keil (she/her)

I.

He was standing in the middle of my dream/So I had to run him over/The world's lack of his eyes/flooded my room

"I'm going to have to let go of you. Of the idea of you," I said, searching his light green eyes for a glint of recognition. Finding none.

"But what if, I'm not ready to let go of the idea of you?" He responded. A smirk, his hand on my breast.

I removed it sadly. "There is no idea of me. There is only me."

II.

Do they leave me
His tired smile on mine
And even once I will just become more
Through every spare second I have
It's not that he sees a cup after cup of full water
6hour phone or two people whose eyes met

Death by moonlight
What's the closest intersection to tomorrow?
Emotional hunger is watching
                                        other things

I just sat and watched the moment. I haven't met you.

I've lost quite a lot, waiting to be shining everywhere else.

Shallow stars in the sky
A memory of tomorrow
Yesterday's imagination

III.

I didn't want to have this
talk

not like this
I wanted to see your face

then let's meet
in person

I can't

I'm sorry

I just can't

I'm scared

Of what

of the ending
of wanting to know
how it ends.

Can you ever

Yes and then
we can say whatever we want
whatever we need to
because we know how it's ultimately

going to End

and how do you
want it to end

With you
taking me back to your home

Fucking my brains out

And then we can end it again and
Again
As many times as we want

That sounds nice he says but be reasonable.
I never am.

IV.

I tell no lies/I lose guys like flies/drop 'em while it's hot/downhill dancing

"If it makes you feel any better, you were pretty hot"
"Pffft, so is half of Toronto"
"Yeah, but half of Toronto hasn't slept with me yet"
"Well, if you work the same kind of game on them as you did on me, it won't be long."

V.

It wouldn't be nearly as much fun, if everyone loved everyone to equal bits.

And there's a darkness at 3am, that I'll bet you haven't found in me. Bare like the branches of a winter's tree.

The silver faucet of midnight.
in just a minute of speaking, you've unwound me.
Once in the moment I never end
bought a dehydrated boy to quench a thirst.
That seed holds such a compact space, seconds from the ground
I always get

A single poem.

VI.

Only a shallow woman
dives for cover under others
High as Icarus in November's flame
my lips are poisoned off

Love is to purge
A Poem about Not

A Lover's Kiss away from the lips of Tornado Season.

Mouth Guard – Maegen McAuliffe O'Leary (she/her)

Every morning I unhinge my jaw
to allow more room for
disappointment in my throat.

I stuff my cheeks with cotton gauze,
soak up errant spittle and ask,
why is wetness so forbidden?

Would I choke if I swallow
my own vital fluid?
Would I drown in my own lubrication?

Would I become a sea of myself,
sloshing too eagerly
against clenched lips?

What I Would Tell Eve – Maegen McAuliffe O'Leary (she/her)

Eat the fucking apple.
They are going to blame you
regardless.

You might as well go to the gallows
with a full belly
knowing more than God.

Uncertain Summer – Stephen Mead (he/him)

Sure tension is genuine, enough heat spreading between
all these words spoken because—
they aren't the ones essential.
Instead fragmentation occurs, an existence image-real
in certain eyes but so false, some living
subterfuge accorded, needed by dreams
with the whole picture frame still ill-fitting.

Hid, closeted in unreachable regions, lethal
leftover smoke is an addiction to consume bowels
nicotine raw—
That's how he smoldered and flaked off, hot ash
for hot ash, uncertain of everything
but the die-hard self, an absoluteness
privately nurtured.

Who said, *"Sick"* facing the myth's death?
Who found a perversion for curing? Picked the tumor?
Hoped for scabs? Still, through it all, if conscientious,
do we understand, really, collective shock? It's beyond guilt,
violence, cruelty, this quietly difficult
and festering surprise.

Who thought, given time, like summer remembrance at its end,
love would commune through the camouflage put on and shattered?
Was such honesty criminal?

Father. Mother. Listen. Look—
Standing before you is an imperfect figure,
no mapped-out plan, no accusation or *"done wrong"* apology.
Here's someone who wants devotion not so unlike yours.
See, any difference is not in feeling,
and when he goes to that lover what oxygen they will be
by positive tender touch!
What mutual affirmation committed to life!

Thus, is he not, without weak alibis' charade,
the son that you wanted? Perhaps yes, perhaps no.
Yet, supplying nothing less than palpable meaning,
this season time wraps, just who in hell should he *act* like?
Someone who, faking control, undermines it,
or someone of essence who simply, as a lie, cannot begin to breathe?

Seeing Is – Stephen Mead (he/him)

To die standing, alive and awake...
To die knowing it, wanting to shun
what forces come mowing,
to find an eye to focus on
before darkness enters...

Perhaps we might like to ask why
death must exist at the hands of violent oppression.
Perhaps there is no real answer except power bouts
and appetites so huge they believe they have immunity.

Through the sleeve, the hoary distance,
this universe is indigestible.

Still what is more genuine than all the children
of every Syria, Lebanon, Africa, and on?

First give names to the faces passing,
then see the likenesses,
really make them your own.

Symphony of the Birds – Bett Butler (she/her)
After Rosemary Catacalos and Li-Young Lee

The soundtrack of this place
is fuss and fury, a sonata
of perpetual noise. Sirens
soloing over rhythm sections
of rumble and thump, a cell tower
buzzing and humming below the audible.
Across a score of interstates
and overpasses, taquerias and bodegas,
power lines run five strands deep
like gargantuan musical staves.

Migrating birds perch there, huddled
in the cold, clustered like chords
or lined up like sixteenth notes
scribing a fluttering melody, constantly
rearranging themselves as if
by an invisible composer editing,
reworking pitch and rhythm.

A conductor cues this avian orchestra
with the dissonant whistle
of an oncoming train, and they rise
as one, soaring, circling, undulating,
a ballet of birds swooping and swerving
in concert, climbing and descending again
and again, finally settling once more
on staff lines to begin anew
their revisions of time and timbre.

If I could know their silent song, could discern
the shape and curve of their unruffled conversation,
perhaps I could tune out the cacophony
and in the stillness, hear the music
that lives in the space between the notes.

Disinvitation to the Dance – Bett Butler (she/her)

"If American women would increase their voting turnout by ten percent, I think we would see an end to all of the budget cuts in programs benefiting women and children."
—Coretta Scott King

In heels that pinch and blister,
we dance the waltz of human rights:
one step forward, two steps back.

In a cotillion rigged against us,
where the many are controlled and exploited
for the convenience of the few,
we dance.

We dance in fields and factories,
our bodies worn and sore, denied
our labor's just reward.

We dance in offices and boardrooms,
voices ignored, contributions overlooked,
ideas disregarded, disdained,
discarded.

We dance in the echo chambers and algorithms
of propaganda and misinformation,
of social media that demands a face filtered and photoshopped
and a body impossible to attain,
so that influencers and merchants of happiness
can sell us one more product promising perfection.

We dance in the streets and all too often
bear the blame and shame for violence against us,
because we dress a certain way
or have too much to drink or simply
walk alone.

We dance in tabernacles where some would wield
the cudgel of religion to deny us agency
of our bodies, our wombs; of who and what we are and whom
we love; of the names we answer to and how we move
in this world.

We dance in courtrooms and in the halls of congress
where the fetus is venerated; but once born,
left to languish in poverty, to struggle in schools
starved for funding, stripped of art and music,
destined to join the perpetual parade of cheap labor.

We dance at the border, fleeing war and famine,
denigrated, denied entry for the color of our skin,
sending our children across alone, just so
they might have a chance to survive.

We dance to the tune of moguls of murder
who make the machines that maim and kill,
lubricating legislators, plying pundits
with hard cash and twisted logic
to justify selling to any sick, disordered soul
the weapons that slaughter our children
in their classrooms.

We are weary. We are grieving.
and we hold inside a smoldering anger,
tinder of a just and righteous flame.

Come stand beside me,
and we'll shed these dancing shoes that have
squeezed and bound our feet for so long.

We'll trade them in for trainers
and we'll walk, and then we'll run
down this rugged road despite the stones

and threats and hurdles thrown our way.

We'll trade them in for boots, and we'll
gather and we'll march with our mothers
and our sisters and our daughters and our friends.

We'll walk, we'll run, we'll march
to the one place our voices will be heard
in the most real and powerful way.

We'll walk, we'll run, we'll march
to the voting booth.

And we'll let no one stop us.

the piano bench – Bett Butler (she/her)

the piano bench with its hard-hinged lid / sat in my grandmother's house in small-town East Texas / banished to summer boredom in that white-hot place, I would bang on the ancient upright / moldering leftover from a shadowy musical past / where she might have played for parlor sing-alongs and plunked out sacred songs for Sunday school / decades untuned, purple-black varnish a petrified crackle / stained wooden keys crowned by chipped veneers of real ivory / their jagged edges bit and cut small fingertips / poor revenge for magnificent beasts felled by poachers / sacrificed in the service of small pianists blissfully ignorant / of the cries of baby elephants mourning mothers murdered for their tusks

the piano bench with its hard-hinged lid / was the pilot's seat for this noisy zeppelin of ivory and wood, wire and felt / providing flawed amusement for a Southern white girl-child, musically inclined / and temporarily incarcerated in a penitentiary of small-town elders / where radios played nothing but Nashville / and pop music was filtered through the sanitizing cheesecloth of *The Lawrence Welk Show*

the piano bench with its hard-hinged lid / was fitted with two Sears catalogs and a sofa pillow so that small elbows could reach the keyboard / and small faces could rise eye-level with the music rack / displaying a musty Methodist hymnal with shaped note heads sprinkled over stair-stepped staves / some ancient and esoteric code of sacred sound / odd confetti left behind by musical celebrants

the piano bench with its hard-hinged lid / yielded decades-old church bulletins and the crumbling sheet music to "Whispering Hope" / ironically the favorite song of my grandfather / who spent his last years shuffling in the dark fog of clinical depression that dogged both sides of the family

207

the piano bench with its hard-hinged lid / yielded sheet music *The Original Charleston* / its syncopated hook nosediving into the complexities of jazz harmony / its cover the colors of Halloween, two youthful dancers in silhouette / holding each other at arm's length, each kicking up a heel, leg bent at the knee / heads thrown back in terpsichorean ecstasy against a spotlight moon hung in skies of lurid orange

the piano bench with its hard-hinged lid / yielded its last and greatest treasure, *W.C. Handy's Collection of Blues, Words and Music Complete (Includes Such Hits as ST. LOUIS BLUES)* / which found its way to the music rack of a moderately well-maintained piano in the suburbs / where hours were spent relishing the piquancy of minor thirds and flat sevenths / singing slightly foreign and deliciously despondent lyrics about a heart like a rock cast in the sea

the piano bench with its hard-hinged lid / was the Ark of the Covenant holding holy scrolls writ with mysteries of sound and fury / was Aladdin's lamp conjuring the genii of jazz / was Pandora's box spewing forth the low numbers on the FM radio dial / where they played Coltrane, Billie Holiday, Charlie Parker, Bessie Smith / kings and queens they were, conduits of god's voice, musical saints scourged and scorned for the color of their skin / relegated to service entrances and freight elevators and too often, places more dangerous / by fools deaf to music's majesty and blind to human worth

the piano bench with its hard-hinged lid / sat within walking distance of the town square / where in 1908 they burned a young man alive / eighteen years old he was, accused of raping a white woman / the lynching made international news / Tad Smith was his name (or Ted) / a thousand people looked on (or two or three thousand—the newspapers could never agree) / a local photographer took pictures and sold them as postcards / proudly inscribed with his name and notice of copyright / online, you can see those images / where farmers, merchants, housewives dressed in their everyday finery / illustrious citizens, church-goers, salt of the earth / stood calmly watching a body and soul consumed by flames / my grandmother was thirteen at the time / her father, a county commissioner, died by suicide five years later / I have often wondered if he might have tried to stop it / or if he was just another face in the crowd

the piano bench with its hard-hinged lid / was the hatchway to escape from that prison of small and wholly unholy worlds / to a precarious and blessedly fluid life of improvisation / where questions remain unanswered, conflicts unresolved, debts yet unpaid / where moments of grace come unexpected, undeserved / and the resolution of dominants is never a sure thing / I wonder what I owe and to whom / for the privilege of living such a life / and I wonder how to atone for sins of the fathers

Mother – Sally Quon (she/her)

She used to travel
before time eroded
the pathways in her mind.

Before she began to forget
where she was, where she was going,

her children.

She used to travel,
filling a well with experiences,
places she'd been,
things she'd seen.

The walls of the well,
slippery with the moisture
of time. No handholds, no footholds,

no rope.

Sliding further and further
into the depths,
memories, like 8mm film
in black and white,
play out on the walls.

She used to travel.
Now she sits in darkness,
in solitude,
watching grainy film
flicker on stone walls,

clapping her hands,
with delight.

When Papi Speaks – Lin Flores (she/they)

It isn't the machismo mustache
or Mexican cowboy act in roll
of tongue accent or mole colored eye—
it follows me like el mal de ojo anklet
can't get rid of it / don't you *know I am
your father* / furrow boxy brow says,
and sun stained brown, red melanin
jaguar warrior boom voice furious
in / *don't slam the door* / in *get your
hands out of your pockets* / and *joto* / to
insult. But not at me.

So, when I wait to come out, I make
mountains of distance between us
more literal than figurative for
years. And on the day, finally I do
it, I pack it tight in English over
the phone:
hey dad, I wanted to tell
you, I'm gay.
And when dad speaks
It's / *I love you*.

Yellow – Alexis Mitchell (she/her)

The only thing lingering on my tongue is this metallic taste of blood. Because I've swallowed a mouthful of blue. And on days like this, I don't know how to jump through the hoops. Instead, I am cemented to the world and a burden to everyone, including myself. Yet all I want to be is yellow.

Nail in the Coffin – Alexis Mitchell (she/her)

I gather the pieces of all my past lives and bury the bones—the remnants of all the people, places, and things that I used to know. But occasionally, I'll have the urge to dig, resurfacing the limbs to scatter in my poems. This is where they'll lay to rest to reveal stories never once told. And fiction isn't really all that fictitious when familiar features appear. Because there's honestly a thin thread between creating a world and the one we undoubtedly feel—so essentially, fiction is fiction until there's an ounce of what's real. So with this spade, I'll disturb the graves—as many as I have to until these pasts are expunged. Who knew a shovel could be as weaponizing as a gun?

i'd unzip my body and let you crawl in. – Alexis Mitchell (she/her)

only we knew how to break off every inch of us and turn it into art. and i had given you every part. from lips to thighs—even an entry through my eyes, unveiling an eternal galaxy. you were handed the keys to all facets of me. every. inner. working. for these bones were your bones. and for what it's worth, i'd suspend every boundary again, if it meant you would hold this heart in your hands.

Maybe – Elsie Dimaandal (she/her)

Maybe I'm a speck.
In your catholic pond.
Embrace it all.
Then sift through
the grave mortal sand.

Maybe I'm a scrap.
In your festal buffet.
Satiate with core
Leave the peripheries
with hunger to allay.

My feet feel the shallow
of the pond.
As it feeds my insecurities,
an inch of shadow is gone.
I'm leaving the trifling
noise of the party.
As it only serves your fixation
with no warranty.

Moon In San Nicolas – Elsie Dimaandal (she/her)

Clouds parting for girl's best friend.
Bending knees as far as River Thames.
Your reflection singing the sun's essence.
A lullaby for an obdurate caldera dent.

One soul is stale by the chaos of sun.
Spending all sweat, yet still unrequited.
The evening comes, you raise your wand.
Wake the unperturbed, now the unabated.
A humming ape of ambered flame.
How It havocs my mind to utter plaints.
Your beauty is hunting for a patent name.
Carving me out into a wicked saint.

I want to gather all the celestial thoughts.
Lay it to drop the ink and not a blotch.
Claim all their lights from heaven's vault.
A crown is rising. You deserved as such.

In la cocina1 before Mass – Javier Sandoval (he/him)

Abuelo poured red desert whisky
Into lamb's milk warmed
By his new young lady

Told me, *Mijo*[2]
Drugs are like gold diggers
They're worth doing
When you're already broke

His sweet young lady scoffed
And leaned against the cracked-stucco wall

He wiped my chin
Before feeding me
The bottle

So drink, Mijo
Drink so you won't cry

Cold
And broken
In church

――――――――

[1]the kitchen
[2] Son

Good luck hiding it – Javier Sandoval (he/him)

like that cold, Colt pistol
shoved back in your drawer—
how it knows in the wear
of its grip, each red time
you've severed yourself from God.

When Asked About Her Absence at Christmas Dinner – Maggie Kaprielian (she/her)

I will not recount the amount of times I flipped
through radio stations, just to fill the void of dull
silence on the car ride into town.

I will not describe the exhaustion of carrying a tree up seven
flights of stairs, all to decorate the dilapidated branches with
tangled lights and delicate ornaments my hands haven't
managed to drop, til they're nothing but shattered fragments
of memories and glass.

I will not tell my relatives from the suburbs how
New York is supposed to be the most radiant
during the month of December, yet I cannot help
but feel withered,
and blue, and all but radiant.

She led me to believe her love
wasn't something seasonal,
rather, constant.

Yet, just like how department store windows
discard their displays after New Year's,
or how television programs eventually
stop re-running sappy, holiday rom-coms,
her infatuation melted out of existence.

And it's tragic;
because if I close my eyes,
I can still picture our heads resting
on each other around the illuminated tree,
just like how things were last year.

So instead of reciting how lonely December 25th feels,
I will simply fabricate and smile, and toast to the
notion of denial, when asked about her absence
at Christmas dinner.

My Grandmother's Pearls – Maggie Kaprielian (she/her)

Margaret,
Derived from the French language as Marguerite
Latin as Margarita
And Ancient Greek as Margarítēs
All equating to a pearl:
A lustrous, gleaming sphere, composed of rich delicacy

I never met the woman I was named after
My father isn't one for telling heart-felt stories around the dinner table
I grew up with a vague figment of who she truly was,
Along with the unanswered question of, besides being in her bloodline,
Why exactly was I named "Margaret?"

What makes me composed of rich delicacy?

As far back as I can remember,
I've simply rejected the eleventh century name
"Margaret" never seemed fitting for the reflection of a girl with imperfections
My fingers repetitively stumble over piano keys
My voice never knows when it's rambling or when it's completely silent
"Margaret" never encapsulated my earnest existence,
Always too elegant and classical for my own mere perception of myself

Instead, I gravitate towards *Maggie*,
Two syllables of pure messiness
Someone of that name isn't expected to go through life as a poised ballerina,

Perfectly executing beauty and elegance on the universe's stage

The peculiar thing is, my grandmother too rejected the name
"Margaret,"
Much preferring *Peggy* and embracing imperfection
Yet I own a polished pearl necklace that was once hers,
Its radiance glowing a projection of everything I am not

When I wear it around my neck, I can hear my grandma's echo,
Her phantom telling me to never take it off,
To fidget with the surface of the pearls when buried deep in agony,
To juxtapose people's unfathomable expectations,
To serve as a reminder that we are something more than delicacy

I never met the woman I was named after,
But she appears in every crack of my voice when I speak
In order to actually get to the pearl, one must look past the
messiness of an oyster,
Washing away layers of aching seasalt
She would be delighted to hear how I don't discard of the oyster,
How I go through life with messiness,
Telling you right here, right now, that my name is *Maggie*.

staring contest – a.j. flora (he/him)

i can't drive
i just barrel down the highway
i run up on curbs and brake too harsh
because i don't care about this car
i don't care that it has to be fixed up
because it won't be
i'm gonna drive it to work and to school and to your house
and it'll be fine
and it'll drive fine and park fine and start fine

but know every time
i sit at a red light
and i stare at it and neither of us blink
i'm thinking about how i could press the accelerator so
hard my foot goes through the floor and throw myself
through the glass
up into the sky
and i would fly
and i would look down and nothing would tether me to the ground
do you know how it feels when the earth lets you go?

it feels like nothing.
it feels like nothing in the pit of your stomach as you don't even
have enough energy to move your foot from the pedal
and your eyes glaze over and every light blurs into a giant mass
it feels like nothing and you're gonna take this car and drive
full speed into the desert and crash into a telephone pole
and leave this goddamn car a fiery wreck
it feels like you're flying.

i'm going home

and then it blinks.

and i lift my foot from the brake
gently.

i lose.

Online – Tammy Pieterson (she/her)

It's fun, isn't it? Running through my fingertips like melted butter.
Roots of the happiness I helped you plant, grow densely on my
timeline. You looked so good on my old account and I'd always
hoped you'd stay there. Your silhouette parades across my screen
and all I can do is give you a double tap to remind you that I still
care. I suppose, no amount of blue light can make you see me now.
So, I just keep scrolling, like you never walked me home that night.
Like I don't know you blame your parents for his death. Like saying
your name in between long sighs doesn't knock the teeth right out
of my mouth. So. Much. Fun.

Breakable Bones – Megan Diedericks (she/her)

It isn't in my bones
to be vulnerable:
I have fallen one,
two, three too many times
and the casting
did not make the break
grow back stronger.

My ribcage,
home to scar tissue,
snapped like a twig
and punctured my air supply.

I have grown desert-sand dry;
I think it might be easier to lie
to people I love
because every time I have to smile
and understand in places I don't belong—
more of me turns to ash.
But guilt is a mountain,
and I carry enough ranges already.

I touch my bones,
and I feel my lungs.
Somewhere a bird once sung
its last outcry,
and I wish I had its wings.

Father – Paytience Ferguson (they/them/her)

Your fingers often brushed the thorns of
the roses, and you would pierce my flesh
to help me feel something other than the
lumps stuck in my throat. How can you
pick yourself up and smell the roses when
so many are trying to bury you
underneath them—when you, yourself,
are digging your own grave?

I am growing stale I'm afraid.

I stare in this mirror, and I am forced to
see my father. I am his child; there is no
denying it. Like father like daughter, I
hate every ounce of myself. Where am I? Why
can't I see me? I have been told to find who
I am, but there are so many parts of me that
I have left behind. The maggots are trying
to escape my veins again, the beetles are
crawling out of the holes I had carved in
my legs long ago.

The memories find comfort in
eating at my brain.

Today I stood on my balcony and imagined
what it would feel like to fly—no I
daydreamed about jumping from this
hollowness of my life and the father I see
when I look into the mirror.

What is wrong with my hands, God? – Paytience Ferguson
(they/them/her)

What is wrong with my hands, God? "To seek and I will find you" but where was the light of the world when I sobbed against the gravel with my nails trying to claw their way out of this Hell?

Where were you before the towers of mine collapsed, my own people, fleeing from the falling constructions? That night I feared nothing of the consequences, just remembering how my throat burned and how I wanted this body of mine to explode with every firework. I want to ask where you were when I sat in the hospital fighting the same war that keeps going on in this head of mine; I do not have the strength to fight this war.

Life just is not that simple is it, my God? Sometimes I still wonder if you like to repeat the scene of the night I sat on the road reaching out for some answer only to be met with numbness in my knuckles and a body that is not my own.

What is wrong with my hands, my God? Why have you become deaf to my screams?

You labeled my legs as an entrance as soon as I was born and when bent: an exit. There are only so many ways to write about being destroyed without declaring the same story, but my body is growing tired of wondering when the fuck I became the subway and why I was taught to understand that my body is not my own, and you did not care.

Sometimes if I squint my eyes enough I can ignore the fact that the bible looks a lot like the man who stamped "Ready" on my soft baby skin that was clearly not. No one had ever taught me how to pray, but there were nights when I got on my knees with no shame and asked God for forgiveness. It was storming, and my fingers shook with every rattle of the sky.

I thought of how the veins of color clashing with the gray
was God's way to show me he heard my resentment, but he took
the hope that I had taken from scripture, and from the looks
of the sky; I am not forgiven.

Forgiveness – Paytience Ferguson (they/them/her)

I stuck my fingers down my throat to shake hands
with the thing that controls me. Slowly but surely, I
think it wants what's left of me.

It tells me to pack my bags and follow in my dad's
footsteps, but each time I stare down at the water I
retreat.

Am I too weak or too strong?

I am unapologetic to deny that the water sings such
a pretty song. I watched my dad try and find
happiness in a bottle and the days he would inhale
searching for sanity.

It felt like when I convinced myself love is accepted
through closed fists and spit; I will forever be
ashamed of the things that will be stained on me
until death.

Even after depression tore apart every part of us, we
sat around and acted as if nothing had phased us,
smiles are meant to be spent and I, I am in debt...

But I don't think I know how to smile anymore.

I know deep down if I had to write a letter of
forgiveness for you, it would look a lot like the
Suicide note that you will not leave, and I do not
forgive you. I cannot forgive you.

My dad and I both have the same addiction to putting
things in our veins that don't belong, but my poison
comes in a blade rather than a heated spoon.

And He Said He Wouldn't Have a Gay Son – Charles K. Carter
(he/him)

He wanted his gay son dead,
so he shot him in the heart with his antique rifle.

He cut his son into pieces and dispersed the parts
inside the bloating stomachs of roadkill along highways 3 and 20.

When the sheriff found a human eye, sea-green, in the buck's
intestines,
the DNR launched an investigation.

They found more and more human remains,
and they thought the deer had become aggressive.

So hunting season started early, and there were no limits.
And he couldn't have been happier to empty his casings upon the
rich Iowan soil.

The Yangtze – Charles K. Carter (he/him)

River of pesticide run-off,
of cereal boxes, needles, and plastics,
of disposable ear plugs, fishing nets,
Styrofoam, and floppy discs.

River of plenty is now running out of life.
Some like it dirty, some like it rough,
but this place is too dirty for some,
so dirty the Chinese sturgeons won't even fuck.

River of porpoise without fins,
big smile, round body thought indestructible
now running out of food
like the baiji dolphin, her sweet dead uncle.

River of purpose, home of the giant softshell turtles,
once viewed as holy figures, as divine deities.
There are only a few left, all thought to be male.
Big money won't stop until they've killed all the gods.

Hunger – Charles K. Carter (he/him)

The dog fighter
keeps his best pit in a small kennel,
gives the animal little water,
no food,
no stimulation
for up to a week before the next big fight.

Throw a small cube of steak in the ring
and see how hunger makes one bare their teeth.

*

It's all a laughing matter
when Petruchio starves Katerina
in order to make her obedient,
to make her a good weak wife.

*

The elephant gets a peanut,
at least when she performs the way she is supposed to.
It's that or the switch, so she carries the acrobats on her back
and she stands upon their stool.

They cheer when she smiles
but that's not really a smile on her face
but a hungry cry for sweet freedom.

*

Candy and hollow threats
are used as a tool to stop the child
from throwing a public tantrum in the store.

Be good and I'll feed you, Sugar.

*

Hunger can be self-inflicted.

Depressed captive dolphins may refuse food,
bash their skulls against their concrete enclosures,
and when they have had enough

they simply choose to breathe no more.

*

Hunger can be self-inflicted.

One day without food. Two days without food.
Give us control over our rotting shells.

Five days without food. I'm searching the mirror for a change.
Give me power in this wasting away.

as the crow flies – Ken Cathers (he/him)

not as straight
as I once imagined

too many distractions
shiny bling
roadkill pate

I am a scavenger
of lies, screamer
of secrets

call it crow music
pain song...

I am malice
that swoops down
from nowhere

a splinter of fear
a splatter of bad news
a friend
          not to be trusted

I am a thief
at the edge of darkness
a muddle of legends

have stolen the moon
feathers dipped in blood
I am everything
you never believed

faint stink of something
the wind blew by

I am a noise
in the darkness
I am the shadow
that follows you home

Icarus – Ken Cathers (he/him)

all I wanted
was to be
that perfect word
      in a poem about water

moving to the secret sway
of tide and wind

wanted the breath
held back
      unspoken

become the lost word
a cloud, a shadow
circling
      above open water

all I wanted
was the perfect
idea of wings

before everything changed
and I fell endlessly
into that shimmering ocean
      of light

Anniversary – Candi Martin (she/her)

There's a goblin in my arms again,
the one that plagues me since you left us.

Painted-ladies flicker,
weave, chase, swoop, then rest together
now, instead of softening
as they water lilac Buddleia,
my arms, chest, stomach, stiffen up
Titanium coat of armour.

I've got that dull droll chaining dark again,
haunting since you left us,
vice-like, all-consuming
disconcerting brain fog.

I've got that sickness in my thighs again,
hips so tired now of not dancing,
weary, stilted, still-cold toes,
sympathetic maybe.

A black-green stretching web-like
around two years of tear worn sockets,
same dark hue that grew around them
just before you left us,

When,
through two months of sleeplessness,
wretched panic, high dose morphine,
my tough cookie pastry self,
fell to crumble,
whilst you whispered
you could see angels.

I've got that gut punch, guttural stomach wrench,
grief-drunk whenever upstanding.
I've got that goblin in my arms again,
the one that plagues me since you left us.

when i think of canada – Linda M. Crate (she/her)

i needed to be broken,
needed to shatter before i
could become me;

but now i remember my voice
and i remember my magic—

i will never allow myself to be
so lovesick i forget who i am again,
will never get so lost in the dream
of what could be that i lose sight of the
present because it's the best gift and
the only one i can open right now;

i fell in love with you because you
reminded me of a girl i loved once—

but she would've never left me
for dead, buried beneath the pines,
hoping that i would just wither and
decay and wilt in all my desire;

so i think it is why it is her i remember
and not you when i think of canada.

so many things i wish i could tell you – Linda M. Crate (she/her)

as i listen to kate bush,
i think of you;

remembering your little pink car
and all of our adventures
like dracula's ball and when i became
a cast member in one of the plays
you produced,
when i came to visit you in erie
and philly both;

sometimes when i listen to vnv nation
or the soundtrack to *repo! the genetic opera*
i think of you also—

but also when i see pink sunsets
or white roses or when i see a girl with pink hair
i think of you and how i wish that our friendship
was still blooming;

i have so many things i wish i could tell you.

i love my strange magic – Linda M. Crate (she/her)

left with so many memories,
haunted by so many ghosts;
i begin wondering when is
forever supposed to end?
because some forevers aren't
long enough to satisfy me,

sometimes it makes me wonder
if my friends will always stay;
or if they will find excuses to
abandon me one day—makes me
wonder who actually likes who
i am; but i fought so hard to become
me that i won't abandon her—

i love my strange magic,
and the lyrics of my heart and soul;
i also love the mythology of my bones
and despite my flaws and imperfections
know that i am worthy of love even if
the only person that will ever love me is: me.

Rebeccan Elegy – Janet M. Powers (she/her)

In this frozen stillness,
in the moment between breathing
and not breathing,
I cannot see the bird.
Many have lost sight of her,
comfort as we mourn:
> sifting through photographs
> setting fingers to bows and keys,
> we speak of music, hers
> how she gave it up for life,
> to teach the whole of it.

In the moment between breathing
and not breathing,
the bird has grown huge,
the sum total of our love:
of cradled sistering
years of sheer daughterness.
> This bird has flown surely
> into the white stillness;
> what was, now soars
> while we, grounded,
> weep slow tears.

Marcia – Janet M. Powers (she/her)

Comes August and incessant rain
whispering to earth after days of drought;
grapes, purpling, hang drenched,
water dripping from papery leaves;
a mallow with great scarlet flowers
has bloomed behind the compost pile.
Morning saw the last two kittens
wet and stiff beneath the kitchen window;
The kittens will go into the earth,
layered under rock and rain-soaked clay.
Like them, you died young,
just finding your nose for wine.
Because they're not yet sweet,
I linger at the arbor with the grapes,
intent on tasting their tart flesh,
a poor penance by the living,
for kittens, for loss, for you.

Forfeit – Kate MacAlister (she/her)

lay down in a bed
of summer's end
of reeds and sand
of a thousand deaths
the last fireflies
grieving for the river
elevated on a free surface
I will sink
drown dreaming
soundly ablaze
dancing on your lips
a confession
"it is not a coffin
it is a renaissance of the moon
and loneliness burning at dusk"
I would unfurl your hands
like withered leaves
delicate and hardened
dried with the heat crushing
at the very end of the world

Are you afraid?

land softly in the fern and moss of my wishing bones

Are you alive?

Phrasing
"my darling"
like a question
it leaves this phantom wound starcrossed on my throat
so oblivious
so obliterated
by my silence

tell me.

does a door stay open
or does it remain shut
if you tear off the handle?
when the sun set
and the path is untaken
kissing in blackberry thickets
scratches and thorns stuck in soft tissue
may be the consequence as *if I didn't know that*
if only this fleeting light could show you
how I fell
on my cursed knees
to drink
your waters.

Bed and Roses. – Kate MacAlister (she/her)

Idk...
I am under a spell
send for demon daddy
or the exorcist
maybe some coffee
and vanilla ice cream
and a cigarette
call for change
while you're at it

will we just lay here?

>   when a storm spills onto the street
>   the hand throwing a rock
>   is holding
>   a first kiss
>   between what is
>   and what could be

injured parties born from
the fire in your eyes
it lights up this dying world

cover me in ashes, darling.

Melusine – Kate MacAlister (she/her)

cut me deeper
as we hide beneath the
floorboards creaking with
your strange rebellion

it is centuries old

my hunger is a shapeshifting
oath a castle of rage and sand
a home full of silver scales
a tidal wave pouring moon
songs

out of my hair
into your hands
a wishing
well
a prayer
holy from the waist
down

at sunset
the long shadows
become blackened pages
tangled in seaweed
where you and I are
sea serpents
sirens
enchantingly
calling for Death
to all men

all that is left
for the ritual is
to collect the husks
and shells

please hold
my sea glass
between the small wrecks
and reefs of your scarred
porcelain fingers don't wash
me out
tomorrow

please hold
my heart in that
vast ocean of your calling
cast on the dark legged sky

witness the
rebirth of Venus in a storm of
salt in my mortal eyes
I don't care about the broken
things we leave behind
Just drive.

Swan – Agnieszka Filipek (she/her)

I rub out the sun with an eraser
glue stars onto the sky
cut out the moon from a National Geographic

I arrange lamps
on empty streets
lighting one at your favourite bench

Fallen leaves
rustle under my boots
collected by the wind

A swan swims in the city fountain
I don't know what he's doing here
alone at night

He's nestling his head in feathers
tucking himself
underneath his wings

All the Souvenirs – Agnieszka Filipek (she/her)

everything tastes better in bed
you whispered in my ear
too many times

I smashed all the souvenirs from the places
you always wanted to visit
shouting out her name

shattered pieces getting deep
into your Persian rug
like knives into flesh

frantically trying to change a hoover bag
and everything else in my life
job flat breakfast cereal

no more take away pizza
from that Italian place
on the corner

we were always forgetting napkins
and you were licking
my fingers

Windows – Agnieszka Filipek (she/her)

another party
in the downstairs neighbours'
drowning out my thoughts

how many pills did I take
I forgot to count again
one two three five seven

my palm can hold thirty-eight
my throat easily
can swallow fourteen

half of my life lost
like hours wasted
looking at your dark windows

Nightcarb – Braden Hofeling (he/him)

They say you shouldn't eat before bed, especially not

carbs, they'll go straight to the thighs. But this

isn't on my mind. What lays on my mind is how simple carbs lay like traps

on teeth, rotting, rotting, and feeding all those nasty bacteria.

I think about how I've rarely ever traded something so permanent for something fleeting, but an exquisite exhilaration leads me to sink my teeth into

the buttery bread.

But what are teeth but bone, and bread but the bones

of wheat? Sometimes a thing seems so disconnected in one light: a tombstone at dusk, and in another, so complete: a tombstone with flowers at dawn in Spring.

So foreign and alone yet, at times, so perfectly paired. Like cheese and wine. Bonnie and Clyde. Death and marriage. These

are the thoughts that keep me up at night.

Like how if you say 'coffin' out loud long enough, you'll start to get the chills or you'll speak until you get it to ring just right.

FICTION

PLACE OF MILK – Renee Chen (she/her)

There was a time when there wasn't war, when red meant roses, and not the wounds of a body, the tingling surge of some things missing, tides of blood out of a broken skin. It was a time when ears still knew music, singing voices and the ebullient magic of them, and not the shots made by guns.

I wasn't born into the war; my brother was. Around the same age when I learned about the fearful avidity before stepping into a river, pants rolled up and tanned skin fondling the water, he learned about a country that was torn apart and sewn back together, stared with his newborn eyes at the seam left behind, jagged scar on the face of an entire people.

In summer afternoons when heat drained down from the sky, like the weight of clothes pressed against a clothesline, the two of us would leave our tents to the adjacent fields. We would race against each other, past timber planks that bridged creeks thick with runoff, plastic, blue tents coated in mold, cans and glass bottles that, like dandruff, dotted dirt paths. Perhaps all the time, scuttling and gasping into the wind, we had really been racing against the world.

"We lived in a house," I would tell him when we rested our heads against our knees, T-shirts cuddled to our chest. "Not a tent." I drew it out on the soil, the heat flickering against my finger. "We lived in a town called Nyamata. Not Zaire."

"Nyamata," he would repeat the name to himself quietly, feeling the weight of the word against his tongue. "Place of milk."

"The place of milk," I said, the heels of his feet pressed against mine. It was what the word meant in Kinyarwanda, our language. "It's why Dad named you Amata," I told him. And also why I always called him Milk.

***

254

Before my mother died giving birth to Amata, we lived in a tall, narrow house with celadon green roofs. It was the most novel, eccentric one in the town, my father had told me, one with orange-plastered walls and grand casement windows in sapphire blue, birchwood frames.

Inside the house, enveloped in between the tang of salted broth and stewed plantains, was a kitchen, where I had listened, humming, to the drums of a metal spoon against a pot, the whacks of a blade against an onion, sliced away like trees chopped by swinging axes.

"There is a whale who brought me out of the sea," my mother sang, her caramel-brown hair tied in a ponytail, the curls cuddled to her back, "and took me to a land where a man met me. We went to a castle, and all was meant to be. There was a door to happiness, and you were the key."

***

The first night when the gunshots came, zigzagged across the flatness of tin roofed houses, pricks of Acacia flower buds, crumbled and collapsed onto dirted doorsteps, my father was away at the hospital. He was there finishing his night shift as the doctor when he hurtled home and took my brother and me into our bedroom, the one at the center of the house.

For hours, I sat shadowed by his silhouette, stared at the flecks of moonlight on his thick, boxy glasses. I could feel the crisping chill from the birchwood planks that made up the floor beneath me, the lacquer thin and glassy, like grass glazed by dew. He hummed to Amata softly, my brother in his arms and the lights above us turned off. Somewhere, someone hollered against destiny.

At midnight, he woke me up. There was a sack on his shoulder, scattered clothes on the bed, splayed out like mustard seeds frying in a pot. But I couldn't see any steam. "We need to leave," he told me.

"But what about Mom?"

He opened the door of the room, his bronze fingers curled up around the doorknob. "She'll be here," he told me, taking my hand in his. We strode out of the house, the darkness descending above us. The patches of clouds were thick, the heat choking the air, its weight like a wet towel. "Always here," he said, a promise.

***

For a time, I hated my brother.

I kept my distance from his cradle at our house, inside my father's room, glaring at him whenever I walked nearby. When he tried to hold my hand, his plump and infinitesimal, I would shake it off, tell him to back off.

For years, I couldn't forget about the evening he was born, at a hospital in Kigali, miles away from our home. I was waiting outside at the end of the hall on the ground floor, the door of the room partly open. I could see my mother lying inside, on a table, beneath a sheet. There was a nurse on her right and the doctor on her left, the air a tang of antiseptics.

The nurse slipped out of the room. "You want to come in?" she asked my father, handing him a gown. He put it on and paced in. I stayed outside, twisting a rubber band with my fingers. The strand of rubber stretched and slipped from my hands, scudded across the air like a stone skimming, scratching the surface of a river.

"You killed my mother," I told Amata one evening, voice deepened by the glare pressed against my face, forehead creased in the darkness and gossamer mist. He laid still beside me, the tent around us flapping in the night.

He thrusted his hands out into the air, fingers clenching into fists. "It's our mother."

"Huh?" I asked, sitting up.

He picked up a rubber band from the ground, twisted it in his hands. "She's mine too."

***

We left Nyamata in the back of a lapis-blue truck of my father's friend.

The truck steered by cascades of people, pilgrims carrying white burlap sacks on rusted bicycles and on their heads, their moans lit by the rising sun.

"Where are we going?" I asked my father as the truck jolted down another dirt path.

"Do you know about the Whale?" He asked me, fanning air against his face, the two of us drowning in the heat.

"The Whale?"

"There's a whale that can fly," he told me, hands splayed out in the air. "It owns a castle. That's where we are heading to now." He turned around and gazed out of the truck, at the gray sky, fallen houses with bullet-punctured walls, a man on the street behind us hobbling down the path, a cane in his hand.

"A beautiful castle," my father said, humming the words into a song, "with a river, a river to swim in. And a house with a green roof, and your mother, your beautiful mother. And a castle, a castle for the four of us."

***

The day my father died at the hospital on the outskirts of the camp, I walked up to the top of the flat, tiny hill at the center of the settlement. Amata was screaming, yelling at me to come back, but I kept on walking, a swarm of sand around my bare feet, shins scarred by weeds.

I stumbled up the soiled path tucked between knots of blue tents, dusted and buried in dirt, past fields of withered corn that never sprouted. Halfway up the hill, rain came down, softly, then all at once.

"Look for the green roof," my father had told me once, "and you'll find the way home."

At the top of the hill, I looked down at the soaked land, a bare-boned child pushing a wheelbarrow down a dirt path, two men trudging across the corn fields. I thought about what he said as I tipped my head back, skin flecked by the falling rain. Silently, I listened to its rhythmic beats against the ground, the rattle synced to my own pulse. But I couldn't find any green-roofed houses.

1984 – DC Diamondopolous (she/her)

James, as the doctors and staff at St. Mark's Regional Hospital in San Diego insisted on calling him, applied pancake make-up over the band-aid camouflaging the skin lesion on his chin. He was glad to be home, surrounded by his Nippon figurines, the ornate lampshades with exotic scarves draped over the top, and his trunk of overflowing satin and silk costumes, boas, several strands of pearls, and oodles of costume jewelry. His move to San Diego had been a windfall—the most money he'd ever made doing drag. He lived to entertain. On stage, he was Jasmine and she was loved. Standing-room only. Now he was sick. How long would he be able to afford his apartment in Hillcrest?

The obituaries from three newspapers spread across the coffee table. Circled in black were the names of seven young men.

Jasmine wanted to live, to work again at Glitter Glam Drag. But James didn't.

No can do, James. You're not going to pull me down today. It's Pride. I'm going to party.

Donna was coming.

At St. Mark's, the only person who bathed and dressed him, changed his sheets and consoled him, was Donna, the pretty dyke nurse who was now his source for food, medication, and shots—his entire life.

It was Sunday, her day off, and she promised to take him to Pride. Jasmine had never missed a parade, but James's taunts of looking butt-ugly opened more scabs than he had on his body.

Jasmine dressed in black sweatpants and a gold lámay blouse, brushed her long stringy hair, pulled it into a ponytail, and clipped it with a rhinestone barrette. She applied red lip gloss and blue eyeshadow.

When James fell ill and admitted himself to St. Mark's Regional, the doctor asked how many men he had slept with. *Was he kidding?* "Honey, how many stars are there in the heavens?" Hundreds, thousands, in parks, bath houses, clubs, from San Francisco to LA and San Diego. The doctor had kept a straight face when James answered. The nurse turned her back on him.

Gay liberation tore the hinges off closet doors. Men like him left the Midwest for the coasts and found a bacchanal of men, a confectionery of sex and drugs, a feast for the starving who thought they were alone in the world.

James's life had been about dick and where to get the next fuck. Jasmine's life was drag, antique stores, and *Vogue Magazine.*

When his conservative, homophobic, fundamental Christian parents caught him in his mother's dress and high heels, they demanded, "Get out now and don't you ever come back." He promised them, "I'll live up to your expectations. I'll make the most of a trashy life."

Jasmine grabbed a green boa from the trunk and wrapped it around her neck. *You think that'll hide your Kaposi's Sarcoma,* James baited. Jasmine tugged at the feathers that made her neck feel on fire.

Grace Jones's, "Pull up to the Bumper" boomed from the ghetto blaster. Jasmine wanted to dance, but her legs ached. *You can't even walk, sucker.*

"Shut-up, James," Jasmine said, pulling herself up and moving to the window.

When he heard a car, he backed out of view. James never wanted Donna to know what she meant to Jasmine.

He held onto furniture as he made his way to the red velvet couch and sat, poised, waiting.

Donna knocked and opened the door.

"Well, don't you look jazzy," she said, pushing a wheelchair inside with a rainbow flag attached.

You'll look like a sick bastard in that baby buggy, James bullied. *Everyone will know you have AIDS.*

"I can't go."

"It's up to you."

"Are we so pathetic we need a parade?"

"Yes," Donna pinned a button that read, *Gay by birth, fabulous by choice,* on his blouse. "We need to pump ourselves up. If we don't, who will?"

"They want all queers dead. Looks like they'll get their way."

"Not everyone. The Blood Sisters keep donating blood, and they're delivering food and medicine."

"Thank God for lesbians," he said and wondered if gay men would do the same if lesbians were dying.

Donna released the footrests on the wheelchair.

"I'm not going. Everyone will know I have AIDS."

"You do, James."

He looked away, not wanting to disappoint the woman who showed him so much compassion and strength.

"What if I run into someone I know?"

"You'll know what to say."

"Like I'm dying of pneumonia. Like all those fake obituaries," he said, kicking the coffee table. "Fucking closet cases. Even in death."

Jasmine felt the weepies coming on. James scolded, *Be a man. Only sissies cry.* But Jasmine was female, too. "In my obit, I want you to put that I died of AIDS. I want everyone to know."

He held onto the seat of the wheelchair and winced as he pulled himself up. The smell of barbecue wafting in from the open door reminded him of summers back in Kansas City, his mom cooking the catfish that he and his dad caught in the Missouri River, his dog Corky—was she still alive?—joyful memories that always left a wake of loneliness.

Today was supposed to be happy, floats with dancing bare-chested boys, banners, dykes on bikes.

Donna shoved the wheelchair forward, "I've brought water and trail mix."

"Poor substitute for poppers and quaaludes."

Donna laughed, pushed him outside, and shut the door.

The ocean air breathed vitality into his frail body. He raised his face to the sun and began to gather life like flowers. A bouquet of drifting purple and orange balloons floated high toward the swirling white splashes in a blue background. He heard applause and whistles as he watched a float pass by on Park Boulevard. "Go faster, Donna. I don't want to miss anything." For just one afternoon he wanted to wave the rainbow flag and cheer the parade on and forget about himself and all the dying young men.

Breathing – Patty Somlo (she/her)

This morning Mary promised herself that she wasn't going to let it get to her. Not the half-tiled bathroom or the electric socket that didn't work behind the refrigerator. She promised herself that she wasn't going to get all worked up and call Mikhail, her Russian landlord, and scream at him until he said, "All right. Let's keep calm."

Her therapist, Sarah, had recently started suggesting medication, something she had never done in the six years Mary had been seeing her and this had Mary worried. It meant that Mary was getting worse.

The worrying had always been there. But lately Mary couldn't find a single spot that felt like solid ground, a place where the earth didn't seem as if it was constantly shifting. She wanted to have a day—just one lousy day—when her life would feel certain, when all the electric sockets worked and the bathroom was nicely tiled and she didn't have to worry about anything.

This morning, though, it occurred to her that no matter how many times she called Mikhail he was going to take his sweet-darned time to fix that socket and finish re-tiling the bathroom wall that was now half-covered with pink tiles and the other half covered with grey fiberboard and the whole covered over with plastic so that Mary and Alan could take showers without the entire mess getting wet. Mary realized that Alan took it all in stride, assured that one day the pink tile would cover over the grey fiberboard, and in the meantime, they would make do. Mary understood that she was ticking like a suspicious-looking package and she had to stop looking to other people and the circumstances of her life to defuse her. Now that Sarah was suggesting medication, Mary knew she'd better get a grip or she would rapidly spiral down the steep slope to breakdown. Once she started careening down that road, she knew the chances of coming back were slim.

263

"Breathing," Mary said, when she was alone in the apartment after Alan left for work.

Breathing. That's what Mary had been taught to do in her long years of therapy. Breathe into the anxiety. Let it be, instead of fighting against it, trying to control every piece of her life just so she wouldn't have to feel so scared.

Breathing in, letting the breath go all the way to her toes. Grounding her to the earth. Last week in therapy, Mary told Sarah how all of her life she had felt like she was just on the edge of disaster. That all it would take was one false move and she would go over the cliff.

Sarah asked her to breathe into that feeling and tell her whatever came up and Mary said she saw herself as a little stick figure, like a child's drawing, walking on a tightrope. That's how she felt every day of her life. Like a stick figure teetering on a tightrope.

Breathing. Mary sat at the kitchen table and looked at the thick orange extension cord running from the refrigerator to a plug at the far end of the dining room. The extension cord had been there for two months while they waited for Mikhail to fix the kitchen socket, and Mary couldn't count the number of times she had tripped over it. Mikhail kept saying he would send the electrician over "tomorrow," but tomorrow never arrived.

As Mary sat with her hands folded loosely in her lap, slowly breathing in and out, staring at the extension cord, she realized it was the hopelessness of the situation that got to her. That she couldn't see an end in sight. She felt foolish getting so upset about a little thing like a broken socket. Why, people lived in far worse situations than this, with rats and leaking upstairs showers dripping through the ceiling. Life-threatening problems. But she could see now that the socket not being fixed was a metaphor for her life, the life she had always been so disappointed in, and hard as she tried, felt she could never fix.

She breathed in and heard Sarah's voice in her mind, what Sarah would have asked if they had been in therapy at that moment. "Talk about that, Mary. Talk about that life you felt you could never fix."

"Oh, but where would I begin," Mary whispered. Where to begin? With the job I hate, just like I hated the job before that and the job before that and the job before that? Or should I talk about the endless track I feel like I've gone around and around and around on? That track where I tell myself, "If I do this, *then* I'll be happy," or "If I do that, *then* I'll be happy." And the endless waiting for this or that to happen. The waiting and waiting and waiting. Like waiting for Mikhail to finish remodeling the bathroom, so I can take a long, slow soak in the tub, listen to Mozart, and finally feel at peace.

"Peace," Mary said, as she breathed in and then let the breath out like a long, loud sigh. Again, she heard Sarah's voice asking, "Peace? What would that feel like to you, Mary?"

And Mary wanted to cry. Peace. If anyone were to ask her what she thought happiness would feel like, that's what she would say. Peace. Like sitting in a chaise lounge doing nothing, thinking about nothing, and not wanting to be any place else but there. And most of all, not worrying.

"Worrying," Mary heard Sarah say. "What is all that worrying?"

It's the voice of doom, Mary thought. It's the voice that warns me ahead of time of the blackness that's about to come. Mikhail will never finish the bathroom and my whole world will turn black. The socket behind the refrigerator will never, ever work and I will never see daylight again. It's sinking, sinking down into the murky depths of the black lagoon. It's drowning. It's being caught in a tidal wave and never, ever getting out.

"So, that's a very sad and frightening place," Mary heard Sarah say. "Have you ever been to that place?"

Ha! Mary wanted to say. Have I ever been to that place? Have I ever been *out* of that place? I know that place all too well. Why do you think I came to therapy in the first place? Why have I been coming to therapy for six long years?

Mary breathed in and remembered the beginning, when Sarah took her back, way back. When Mary couldn't talk about what had happened to her and so Sarah asked her to breathe in and out and then describe the images she could see. Mary remembered the day she saw the image of herself, but she was an egg, not a woman, with huge eyes that took up nearly all the space on her egg body. And the eyes flitted back and forth, all around, looking for danger, trying to keep her safe.

It took a long time for Mary to remember that her father hit her. It took a long time for her to remember that he made her sit at the dining room table and keep her hands there while he whacked her with a sterling silver soup ladle and called her a moron. It took a long time to remember that he hit her harder if she cried, so she made sure not to cry, and that afterwards when her hands throbbed from the pain and sometimes her arms felt numb, he made her finish her dinner, even though whatever she ate would come right back up, and then he would hit her again and make her clean up the mess she had made.

Mary had re-lived those scenes so many times these last six years they didn't seem to have the hold over her they once had. And, yes, her life had gotten better. She had Alan now, who loved her in a way Mary never could have imagined a man might love her. Mary didn't have to cry every day now or sit alone in her room because the gloom felt too thick for her to move.

But there was still this edginess that Mary couldn't seem to shake. She wanted to blame her landlord, but she knew that even if he fixed everything, something would happen to make her worry that she was just about to step off the cliff.

"Breathing," Mary said. "Breathing. Breathing in to feel fear. Letting the fear just be."

This is what she had to do. Just let it be. She closed her eyes and imagined herself on that tightrope but instantly the image shifted to a childhood one, to a dream that haunted her for years, that woke her screaming in the night. In the dream image, Mary was a small girl walking across a bridge and it was very dark. The bridge went over a lake, a lake that was misty and black. Dark arms reached out of the lake toward Mary and the hands grabbed her, trying to pull her down into those murky depths.

As a child, Mary always woke up screaming before the hands ever pulled her down. As she watched the image in her mind now, she realized that she had been fighting against those hands her whole life, fighting to wake up before they succeeded in dragging her down to their world of darkness.

But sitting at the kitchen table now, a woman of nearly fifty, she watched that in her mind. And before she knew it, she had let the hands pull her down, down into that dark liquid abyss. She was surprised to see that the water was warm and she didn't sink. The water was warm and she was rocking gently.

And then she noticed a pair of arms holding her, and she felt sure those arms weren't ever going to let her drown.

Breakfast in Alaska – Jordan Nishkian (she/her)

1:33 a.m.

Although exhausted from her flight, Mira found herself staring at the flat ceiling of her motel room, taking in the bitter smells of tobacco and Pine-Sol. Despite the blackout curtains' best efforts, a sliver of midnight sun had made its way into the room, paving a road for tight-packed dust motes to travel across her disheveled sketchbook on the table, to the pile of yesterday's clothes next to the bed, then over the bridge of her crooked nose.

She debated movement—lying still enough might coerce the sleeping pill she took a few hours ago to re-affect her, but she had to be up in four hours anyway. Getting up now would allow her to enjoy one of those 24-hour diner breakfasts her seatmate on the plane told her so much about.

Mira blinked at the ceiling one last time to see if her eyes, still slick with sleep, would decide for her. Upon reopening, she sat herself up, feeling her bones restack themselves after spending a few hours on an unfamiliar mattress. Toes and ankles crackling on her way to the window, she parted the curtains a few extra inches, instantly inviting sunlight to flood the room and illuminate her skin. Squinting, she tried to wake herself up by taking in views of an aqua sky, tall wilderness, and a weathered sign for the Fairbanks Choice Inn.

"Fucking Alaska," she muttered, half-laughing as she turned toward the small coffeemaker beside the TV.

2:16 a.m.

Mira eased her back onto the red vinyl booth as she stared at the near-empty road. The diner was only a short drive from the inn—almost too short for her rental car's heater to fully kick in. Her thumb picked at the peeling laminate of the menu. It was a nice enough spot to kill an hour.

Keeping her eyes on the scenery, she pulled her sketchbook and pencil case out from her canvas satchel, only turning away from the window when she saw the reflection of a smiling server approaching her.

"Here's that coffee," the server said as she set down a steaming mug. "Mind if I ask what brings you to Fairbanks?"

Mira looked up at the woman next to her, noting her neat-enough ponytail, a silver locket around her neck, and an ironed but faded apron with a nametag that said "Laurel." Her nails were short and practical, and she kept her makeup down to a thick layer of mascara and tinted lip balm. Mira wondered if she would be able to replicate the blue in her irises as the strong scents of coffee and Laurel's jasmine perfume filled the booth. A man wearing a navy cardigan at the counter glanced over his shoulder at them.

Mira's fingers parted the center of her sketchbook and laid it flat on the table, "Is it that obvious?"

Laurel shook her head. "No, not like that," she said. "I'm just good with faces and I haven't seen yours yet."

She paused, head patiently cocked.

"Oh, in town for work," Mira responded and reached for her coffee. She eyed the diner—aside from her and the man at the counter there were only a few booths full of patrons—not many opportunities for late-night conversation. "I have a commission about an hour out from here."

"Pleasant Valley?"

Mira nodded, distracted by a glint of sadness in her eyes.

269

"So you're an artist?" Laurel poured her eyes over some sketches Mira had done of some lingering souls on a train ride. She found purpose in drawing the unseen; the ones that stayed on long past their stops.

"Just good with faces," Mira answered, flipping to a blank page. "Do you like the pancakes better or the waffles?"

Laurel looked back into the window of the kitchen. "Well, normally I'd say pancakes, but Joe's working tonight, so I'd go with the waffles."

"That sounds good."

"He makes homestyle ones, so they're thinner and a little crispy."

"My favorite." Mira handed Laurel her menu.

"Berries on top?"

"Yes, please."

"You got it." Laurel nodded before returning to the register at the counter.

2:41 a.m.

A glass vase with a faux carnation cast a prismatic speckle across the page as her graphite lines began to take shape. She switched out pencils as her hand danced between weaving the thick woolen strands of his sweater, his thinning but glistening head of hair, the buoyant arcs of his profile, and the gentle creases around his smiling eyes. Her glances flitted between the paper and her subject, pausing only to take a sip of coffee or a bite of syrup-soaked strawberry.

She studied how he took up his space. He sat on the stool as if it knew him, cradling the left sole he perched on the footrest without resistance or hesitation. There was no need for him to hunch over the counter for his elbows to meet the laminate surface, and the red-lipped mug curved into the grasp of his sun-worn hands. Although his body was at rest, his eyes were locked on Laurel, darting and pivoting as she moved around the dining room, until she finally paused on the other side of the counter, close enough for him to touch her. Mira wondered if he'd try.

The stool creaked as he looked to Mira, then back to Laurel. Mira's hand extended the line of the counter and began molding the negative space beside him into the shapes that made up Laurel and her posturing.

3:02 a.m.

Her plate emptied as her paper became trafficked with more lead, adding highlights with a swipe of her eraser and shadows with the tip of her finger. Satisfied, she sat back up and pinched her shoulder blades together, realigning her spine with a crescendo of pops. She tore the page away at the perforated edge, lightly folding down the center.

She glanced over to the front counter. The man had gone, replaced by a trio of friends recovering from a long night with milkshakes and pie, and Laurel was grabbing two full plates of food from the kitchen.

"I'll be right over with the check," Laurel said as she hustled to the other side of the diner.

"No worries, I got it," Mira answered as she pulled a twenty from her wallet and placed it on top of the folded sketch at the edge of the table. She finished her coffee with a final swig, repacked her satchel, then stood to make her way to the exit.

271

"Thank you!" Laurel called, still at the other booth. "Have a good morning!"

Mira grinned and waved as she walked out into the chilly April air, fighting a strong gust of wind while she rushed to her rental car.

From her parking spot, she could see Laurel approach her booth to clear the table. Mira watched her expression shift from a curious smile to an awestruck, quivering lip. One hand holding the sketch, one wrapped around her locket, Laurel turned to face where the man had been sitting, then back out the window.

A whir sounded from the heater as Mira began backing out of the small parking lot, avoiding Laurel's eyes as she rushed for the front door.

Sacred Lies – Alice Baburek (she/her)

A yellowed night-light glowed against the peeling wallpaper. The scent of Old Spice lingered in the stale, smoke-filled air. Suddenly, the elderly man sat upright on the sagging mattress. Drops of sweat beaded on his naked chest and lined his graying brows. His paper-thin pajama bottoms stuck to his sticky, hot skin. Thom Stark had had the same disturbing nightmare many times before. In fact, he had it so often, he dreaded falling asleep each night. His doctor blamed it on the heart medication, a rare side effect afflicting only a select few. But Thom knew differently. This consuming nightmare wasn't concocted from the induction of chemicals—but from something much more horrific. Deep inside his acidic psyche hid a dark, horrifying secret. Long before his adoring wife of many years had passed away. Long before his crippling heart attack. And long before he became a decrepit old man.

It began in 1958, that ungodly year that changed his life forever. St. John Apprentice was one of the few remaining reform schools during the late fifties. A religious, holier-than-thou institute intended to restructure troubled boys.

Thom was a good boy—adventurous, ambitious, rebellious, inquisitive by nature. A typical 14-year-old adolescent. But his strict and arduous parents saw otherwise, giving in to their disturbing, twisted mindset, swayed by infectious religious beliefs.

It was there Thom Stark had lost his living spirit, virtually crushed, then dauntingly smothered to the point of no return, whereby his shadowing growth into a man had been beaten down incessantly by the exploitative wrath of an unforgiving god.

St. John Apprentice wasn't an ordinary reform school. It was prelude to hell on Earth—a dwelling of horror for misfits. Thom did not understand nor comprehend the evasive action his parents took that dreadful day in June when they handed over their only son. The frail boy wept that night as he lay alone in a tiny, damp room, shivering under a thin, tattered blanket. The stained, worn mattress, held up by a few broken springs, poked and jabbed into his young, delicate skin. Thom felt betrayed by the two people he held so close. Yet neither one gave him an explanation or justification for their appalling decision. Soon, he would learn the hard way—life at St. John Apprentice was not a life at all.

Thom learned immediately Father Riderbach was the ultimate authority. His six-foot two, immense frame towered over the frightened and misguided boys. Even though Father Riderbach neared the sixty-ish mark in age, his broad shoulders and athletic build intimidated his victims. The silver streaks in his short black hair were always cut close to his oval-shaped head. His thick pair of brown glasses perched on his slender nose hid the true evil that lurked within. His flowing black robe with dark, pearly buttons was pulled snugly around his muscular physique, enhancing his aura of superiority. And for the last twenty years, Father Riderbach reigned with vengeance over his own mortal kingdom, seeking to break the core essence of the virtuous and pious destined souls.

At first, the mighty priest would sermonize to his flock of youthful lads on the wickedness of their ways. But the children quickly came to realize how Father Riderbach controlled them with hard, mean, and unrelenting retaliation if his rules were broken.

It came to be Thom would suffer the horrific consequences of speaking when not spoken to. This was considered taboo and instilled into each of the children as one of the top ten commandments imposed by the powerful and governing dictator.

Thom's split lip and bruised, swollen knuckles were soon ignored as he spent the next several tortuous days and nights down in the catacombs with the dead. Down within the extreme dampness and cold ruins, Thom huddled near the heavy wooden door, which slammed him into another terrifying world. A bed made of smelly straw, and a scratchy blanket to keep him warm. Only three tall candles lit the dungeon of graves from the past. With two loaves of stale bread, a basket filled with rotten fruit, and a jug of tainted water, Thom portioned his inedible rations with care. He prayed each night would be his last in the dank and dismal caves of the holy and long forgotten. But true to Father Riderbach's word, on the seventh day, the traumatized and broken boy was released with a threat of return if not heeding the father's ultimate religious rules.

Hence Thom, like the others, tried his best to keep in line and abide by the almighty priest. Academic classes were few, but laborious work was plentiful and intended to cleanse the wretched soul. And as they grew older and into manhood, there came a sense of rebellion for the virtue and purity that was snatched away with their enthusiastic, youthful aspirations.

Year after year, Thom learned to despise, then hate the man who hid so cleverly behind the distorted, sacred lies of punishment instead of forgiveness, the man who stripped him of his dignity and scarred his very impressionable being.

As Thom reached his eighteenth birthday, he vowed his allegiance with many others to finally put an end to this sadistic reign of terror. Deception became easy, and so did the act they conspired to commit.

So, on that fateful, misguided day, as they all stood emotionless while St. John Apprentice burned freely to the ground, no one heard or chose to hear the cries for redemption from far below. Flames of red and gold stretched into the twinkling night sky, as if hell had opened up and swallowed its awaiting and last judged victim. When it was finished, with battered and beaten spirits, these young men made a sovereign pact never to confess their ultimate mortal sin.

Father Riderbach's body was never found. In fact, there was not trace of him anywhere within the mounds of putrid ash left behind.

Now, many years later, a marble headstone stands in the place where St. John Apprentice once sat. Etched in black letters across its face reads: "Father Ethan Riderbach—May he rest in Peace."

And sometimes on a starry, starry night, when the trees sway and browning leaves rustle from the softly flowing winds, the faint, weeping cries for forgiveness can still be heard as they echo endlessly against the haloed heavens above.

Flaming Leaves – Ben Umayam (he/him)

It was late in the afternoon and me and the husbear were discussing what was so mysteriously upsetting, when Fred called. She had a guy name. But she was a gal. She and her lover, Ginger, were retired, living in this mountain town since 15 years back. She used to manage an all-you-can-eat Chinese buffet place in Mississippi. Ginger was a security guard. They decided to study IT and got in before it was the popular thing to do. "Made a shitload of dough," Fred puts it. "Enough to retire here at 59. Haven't left since."

They play in the snow during ski season, camp and canoe all over in the warm months, even though Fred has had both knees replaced, Ginger, one hip. They invite us to join them every weekend. We decline, "You won't catch me sleeping in a bag on the forest floor, not at my age," exclaims the husbear.

Ian tells me why Fred called, "That forest fire, above Canyon Road, that's near their house, maybe 1500 yards away. The sheriff has not told them to evacuate. He has told them to prepare. Fred wants us to attend their fire party." Like the camping trips, we decline. We are on the way to Denver for a concert.

***

"The mysterious thing," rants Ian, "I thought all those yelling crazies, demonstrating at Planned Parenthoods, that they were far right religious nutzos. At mass here, all these older Catholics like me are now rallying to the new message, the sanctity of life. Today, the deacon, he is not even a priest, he prayed, 'dear god, please let our politicians heed the words of Christ regarding the sanctity of life.' Since when did Christ say anything about inseminated zygotes? They wear t-shirts, 'Summit County Catholics for the Sanctity of Life.' Bet they have 'God Made Adam and Eve not Steve' tees in their closets. What stops some bishop or monsignor, dressed in a dress, from whipping them up against the gays so they can fundraise money, money, money. Can you believe it?"

I can believe it. I am not the religious guy my spouse is. He is a devout Asian Catholic, who goes to church and has faith. Me, I have dabbled in atheism and agnosticism, an outlying follower of Ronald Reagan Jr.

Ian repeats Fred's invite. "She says to come over tonight. Pot-luck dinner. A Fire Party, like those December Pearl Harbor parties you threw in the 80's. We bring the food and help them pack. Just in case. You know they have that huge field, below the forest line, above their house. I think the sheriff's office is just being over cautious with people. I dunno, or is it like that volcano on the Canary Islands, lava flowing into the swimming pool, people running screaming from their home. Did you see that on YouTube?"

I nod that I did.

"Sweetie let's get packing if we are going to make that Denver bus. A knapsack and that is it, we might not have time to spare. Lordy Lordy, *Je suits* fatty gay," Big Darlin' is checking himself out in the mirror. He is getting fatter since we moved here. It is a line from Will and Grace that he is using a lot these days. A Jack line. A play with words. *Je suis fatigue.*' Fatty...gay...get it. Seems you always need to explain gay speak.

***

We return the next day. The concert was cool, a walk through Denver is cool. The big clouds cooling the mountain air.

I am new to this nebulosity. Ian is from these parts. A refugee from Vietnam, raised here in Colorado. I remember when we first met in NYC, he used to say that in New York, he could never figure out where he was. "In Colorado, you knew where you were by looking where the mountains were, you knew to go east or west." I had thought that was poetic, lost in New York because there were no mountains. Ian is always terrible with directions. In the car, I navigate, he drives. GPS, those are my middle initials.

The bus trip is an hour and a half long. Time flies. Because of the clouds. The big fluffy ones, they are cumulus. The others, they are different. Full yet thin and foreboding. The mountains are snowcapped. They stick up above the foreboding clouds. The tops have frosted while we were gone.

"Do you smell that. Like burning tires, no more like wood. That forest fire, it must be getting put out. Those clouds, they look like rain. Could've rained here earlier. If not, it is sure to rain later, those clouds have that look."

I follow what Ian says. But as we get closer to home, I see what looks like campfires that have been put out. There are three giant columns of fumes. Looks like that's where the forest fire was. This is confirmed by the grey smoke we see when we get home, up in the hills, at the tree line, above the fields that separate from the line of homes.

In the evening, from our terrace, we see the orange flare up and smolder as the steady rain falls. The wind seems to be helping, blowing the right way, or maybe the wrong way. Who knows, the flare up of yellow and orange blends with the popping colors of the Aspen in late September in this neck of the woods.

The next morning, I wait for the bus for morning java at the café. The clouds are all shapes and sizes and more like a mist. Above the ridge I see what seems to be a cross peeking out of the mountain top. The misty cloud slowly dissipates revealing the cross is part of a powerline tower. Attached to the complex is a giant cell phone spire. The wind blows the right or wrong way, and the cross is a cross and then, no longer.

Ian calls me, "Come back home, now," he demands. Fred and Ginger have left town. Their home, completely burned down, to the ground. The field between the forest and their mountain home did nothing to stop flames from leaping to the 15-year-old, dry cabin.

Walking up the hill from the bus stop, I hear it first, chomp, chomp, chomp. Then I see the big 'copter. It looms, white all over, black at the back with propeller on top, a helicopter that almost looks like a giant mechanical dragonfly. Have you ever heard dragonflies hovering over a field at the end of summer? It is this dangerous buzz. The helicopter flies to the lake, the reservoir, fills up with water, then flies to the fire sight and drops all its water.

I open the terrace door at home, to show Ian. He covers his ears. "The sound of evacuation. I saw those choppers on tv. During the war, those choppers meant getting people out. Here they mean keeping people in."

Ian is pissed. Fred and Ginger, they have thrown in the towel. They are off to some place in the Caribbean, an island under the hurricane belt. They want to hide from natural disasters. Their house is gone, all burned down.

"What are you so pissed about?" I tell him, we are not changing our plans. It is roughly 6 weeks since we arrived here, six-month retirement plan in the mountains, six months in Europe. We are not going to give up on this retirement plan.

The phone is screaming. It is a pink phone. The manufacturers call it red gold. So that men will buy that color, no doubt. But no mistaking, it is pink. It blasts that horrible signal, the one you get for an amber or flash flood alert. It pierces. Once at mass, Ian says, the whole church, their phones went off. Father Steven kidded, "that is God's way of saying silence your cell phones." The congregation giggled. Ian did not. "Fr. Steven always jokes like that, to emphasize some doctrinal point I guess."

The chomp of the helicopter and the screeching alert, saying it is safe to go back home, pushes Ian to a momentary frenzy.

He grabs the phone, throws it out the terrace door.

He screams his high-pitched gayest scream, short, shrill. And then he calms down. He shrugs. "I aimed at the Aspen trees."

We will find the phone later, out on the bed of Aspen leaves, fallen with their fiery colors of yellows and oranges, sanguine, vermillion.

Strange Encounters – Eric Knowlson (he/him)

On the street, a woman carries a box of groceries from a nearby health-food store. A man hustles towards her going the opposite direction. The woman gently strolls, admiring the spring-time flowers. A plum blossom catches her eye. She stops to look. The man has been staring at his phone. He's just sent a text to explain why he's late. He glances at the time, and shaking his head, picks up his pace. When he looks up, there isn't enough time to stop. She notices him careening towards her, but only after it's too late.

Like a speeding asteroid hitting a slumbering planet, they collide. Debris from the collision explodes around them; papers from the man's briefcase, sweet potato chips from a torn bag, oranges, gluten-free noodles, a thousand grains of rice, and the box that contained them.

She shakes her head in frustration. He brushes rice from his suit and is about to yell. Yet, when their eyes meet, they freeze. His mouth falls agape, and her frown washes away. They are shocked, mesmerized by the familiarity of each other's faces, yet perplexed by their inability to recall how they're acquainted. It's a moment when the diligent hand falls from the face of the clock and leaves two strangers in a space ungoverned by time. The fruit, papers and food are suspended in orbit around them.

The woman's eyes shine brilliantly—like recently unearthed rubies, once lost to desert sands, but now reflecting sunlight again. Their opulence sears into the man. He feels exposed, naked, as if all he is, was, and ever will be is on full display. However, this vulnerability is not unpleasant, on the contrary it fills him with an oddly familiar warmth and a notion that he has returned home.

The woman feels it too: she finds her lips curling into a smile, a smile reserved for only the most intimate of lovers. Her heart flutters with an excitement that's both familiar and untamed. That obscure sense of longing that's been present for all her life is finally satiated. She's never believed in past lives, soul mates, or anything beyond the physical world, yet she can't shake the feeling that their lives are bound together by some unseen force.

Their hearts pump, their veins cough and sputter, dispelling the dust of dull years and making way for forgotten and perhaps forbidden feelings to flood through them. This frozen moment stretches onward and a deep intimacy encompasses them. The swell of pupils growing, smiles, and the subtle twitch of eyelids composes a drama in a language only they can comprehend. Together they live, laugh, love, and grow. A lifetime passes between them and then—

Then time suddenly restarts. Their items clatter to the ground and the world begins turning again. Cars honk. Dogs bark. People step around the detritus of their collision.

The man scratches his head and attempts to form words, but only odd syllabic noises fall from his lips. The woman rapidly shakes her head back, forth. She exclaims, "What the hell was that?" It's less of a question and more of a statement expressing her bewilderment.

"I've missed you, I—" the man starts to say, but then realizes something. "I don't—I don't know you, do I?"

She shakes her head, but her eyes betray disbelief. They may not have met before, but how can they say they don't know each other? That simple eye gaze, lasting only a second, contained as much beauty and depth as an entire relationship. "No, but we know each other, now," she pleads.

This isn't good enough for him. This is something he simply can't accept. It's not rational. He tears through his mind searching for any memory of her, searching for the relationship they shared, but all he finds is a half recollection that fades like the visage of a dream. "No. No, I knew you, I—" his words collapse with despair and he buries his face in his hands.

Watching him she feels a stab of pain. Their moment was barely born before it was whisked away. The loss is grueling. She wants to collapse into his arms and be held. She reaches out and touches his arm. He looks at her ring and then up at her, his eyes display a heavy disappointment.

"Maybe in another life?" she says questioningly.

"Yeah, maybe," he says, straightening himself up. "Or maybe there was a mistake. Maybe destiny ran late…"

Her eyes widen. Melancholy washes through her. She can't consider this. Instead, she tries to take comfort in the moment they shared, the moment that will always be theirs. Their moment ringing out into eternity. Their moment that's already gone.

She decides she has to go, but to leave now feels like a betrayal. She knows she shouldn't, but she feels guilty. And she knows, it's not for her husband's sake, but for this man—she feels as if she somehow cheated on him by getting married. She shakes her head and begins to rapidly gather her belongings, flinging them into a pile.

"Here, at least let me help you pick up your things," he hands her the box and fills it with her groceries. He picks up his briefcase and shoves his papers inside; the job he was rushing to, his work, it all seems so inconsequential now. She thanks him, nods, and turns before she loses her nerve. As she walks away, she fights the urge to spin on her heels and run back to him.

He wants to chase after her but knows it's better to let her go. He's dismayed until he realizes his phone case is missing. He'd somehow only grabbed his phone, not realizing it had fallen out of its case. The phone-case is his wallet containing his ID and all his cards. It wasn't on the ground, so it must be in her box. "Hey wait," he turns, but she is already gone.

He smiles. Maybe destiny was right on time, he thinks. Surely, she'll return his wallet, right?

An Ideal Lost in Night-Mists – LindaAnn LoSchiavo (she/her)

Blood's Kiss – November 2nd nightfall

I learned to be immortal from blood's kiss.
He taught me how to be a ghost part-time.

Like trees, we've bound ourselves below without
Burial, cocooned in soil, still sentient,
Possessed of appetites, required to feast.

Count D.'s companion now, all time dissolves.

Acquainted with the night, ageless, preserved,
We visit after dusk for sustenance.

My roommate Megan looks surprised. I smile.
Her armature is shifting. She's obsessed
With curiosity—the how and why.

First we embrace. She's glad to see I'm safe,
While mentioning police, strange questioning,
Their sketch created for the poster. "Here,"
Says Megan. "Take a look." I move in close,
Bestow my greatest gift: eternity.

Missing, Classified as Undead – November 2nd afternoon

Hallowe'en decorations still dotted their dorm, achingly orange,
when detectives filed in, rust running off the hinges like fresh blood.
Handmade missing posters, plastered with the police sketch, fueled
the hums that wouldn't quiet, unplugged from the lyrics sung to
welcome discovery.

Present for their Q-and-A: Megan, a roommate paired via lottery,
neither confidante nor co-conspirator. She who was absent—
Annabelle—left no trace. According to biblical interpretations, no
harbingers of menace had loomed: addictions, failing grades,
anorexia, bizarre online screeds. Evidence cleaved no flesh from

283

bone: her purse placid on a pillow, no signs of forced entry, no signs of a struggle with a bogeyman lured by heat.

Their dorm room now a photographed crime scene, tension divides Megan's mind in a desperate rush and roil. Who? A guy they trusted? Or a serial killer who'd return to claim Megan next?

Investigators prod her to travel backwards, like storytellers, recounting the last time Annabelle was heard from. They scrutinize the wall calendar, Nov. 1st, All Saints Day, its childish scrawl: "Count D. / Volodya / Vova — 8 PM meet-up" and a crumpled, discarded October page peppered with male names like buckshot, the detritus of dating apps.

Cooperation is truth enveloped by a stringent sun. But facts forget the night harbors its own dialect. Words withhold her odd dream— surely that's all it was. Ushered in by a malodorous air of ancient dirt and gravecloths, a shape-shifting bat flew in, its enormous wingspan not unlike a black satin cloak. Megan squirreled under blankets, the room blotting to utter darkness. "When my alarm clock rang, I saw my roommate was gone," is all she'll tell investigators. They leave.

Alone now, in bed, on edge, Megan hears a loose floorboard creak, notices Annabelle's closet door ajar, as if something's slipping through the in-between, staking virgin space as if this was an outpost of an empire about to be invaded. Megan floods the room with the harsh, institutional fluorescent fixture they've rarely used. Rifling through empty shoeboxes, she spies a diary whose locked flap yields to scissors, unbound by promises. Print-outs from chats shiver her full awake, compel her to read these artifacts, fascinating as a mummy's tape unraveling.

Count D: Do you believe in fate? In an *ideal lost in night-mists*?
Lady A: Kewl.
Count D: Child, you are salting my wounds with capricious teasing.
Lady A: Tell me yr name irl—the one behind yr screen name.

The stench of mildewed autumn leaves makes her look around. Annabelle is watching her.

Dating the Undead — October 29ᵗʰ evening

His dating profile states he's a Virgo with Scorpio rising. He owns a castle, digs "blood diamonds," and he's 7,398 kms away from me.

First off, he asks about my blood type, if I've ever been anemic, if I sleep with my dorm window open, and if I consider myself to be an *adventuress*.

I message him back, coyly requesting pics...inside this castle. I ask: do u really live in Transylvania a.k.a. Romania? If so, how would we meet up irl?

He replies I must never worry—he can be at my doorstep in a flash.

Sure. Ha-ha, I type, playing along. Send pics of u with yr castle, I repeat.

Instead he sends pics of his jewelry vault and apologizes that his selfies rarely come out right. He explains that the thing about modern photography is that it's been stunted by the cowardice of credulity. He adds an smh.

Obviously, he's seen many profile pics doctored with PhotoShop or massaged with beauty filters. I'm about to check which pics I uploaded this week. Instead I Google Transylvania —Wow! Snow-capped peaks!—and ask if he skis or hikes.

He replies his castle is near the Carpathians but forces of destiny conspired to make him fonder of flying than bipedalism, none of which diminishes his enthusiasm for athletic ingenues.

A new pic pops up—a black and white sketch, all smoky charcoal— his dark eyes deeper than the diving pool on campus. Even from

285

here they manage to pierce my composure. His clothing is outdated though elegant—from a high-end vintage shop. Like the ones in SoHo.

As if he's reading my mind—but *how could he?*—he admits to being "an old soul, a connoisseur, a poet manqué." Collecting leather-bound autographed volumes of poetry, he adds, is a consummate delight.

Expecting he'll ask about my faves, I'm recalling which poets I've read in class. Instead he sends me an autographed flyleaf signed Mihai Eminescu, a name I've never seen on the gram.

Then he posts a poem. Probably it's better in the original than what Google translates. Still the first four lines are sweetly romantic and I send them back in English:

> *Oh, ideal lost in night-mists of a vanished universe:*
> *People who would think in legends—all a world who spoke in verse;*
> *I can see and think and hear you—youthful scout which gently nods*
> *From a sky with different starlights, other Edens, other gods.* *

He asks: Do you believe in fate? In an *"ideal lost in night-mists"*?

I text back "kewl."

He replies that I am salting his wounds with capricious teasing. OMG, I think. He *is* a poet. Now I want to know his name irl—instead of his screen name: *Count D*. Honestly, that D made me wonder if it's a new code for "expect dick pics." But he's not a creep. Sure is different tho. And while he's typing, I Google "Virgo with Scorpio rising" and one post says this: "A Virgo Sun Scorpio Rising definitely wants an obsessive love where they will be hooked on the object of their desire." *Obsessive love*! Bussin'.

His name irl bubbles up on my screen: Volodya. WTF?

Then he adds his Mom calls him Vova and do I like his nickname?

"Lit!" I reply.

He keeps texting faster now, at an unnatural pace. Almost like he's telepathing instead of typing. Weird but flattering. Not like the cut-n-paste crap some guys send to every chick. We flirt. He's seductive but never nasty. Kinda thrilling in an eerie way. I imagine his long, slender fingers removing those gaudy rings and caressing my face. I blush and I'm relieved he can't see me—until he asks why I'm flushed. Do I have fever? Am I fully vaxxed?

Before I can reply, he types a question: Do u have plans for Samhain?

I admit I do—but just with friends who have an annual picnic on Hallowe'en on their roof deck. It overlooks Sixth Avenue, so we can watch New York City's costume parade.

There's a long pause. I wonder if his WiFi disconnected up there in the Carpathian Mountains, or wherever he's texting from.

Then he's back. The 30th is his special number cos he was born on the 30th of August, he tells me. It would mean a great deal if we could meet up tomorrow, on October 30th.

Again, I have plans, which is the point of dating apps, am-i-right? But we're super vibing. I don't wanna be a downer, so I ask: Nov. 1st? It's crazy but suddenly I feel a jolt through my cell, a surreal tingle through my veins.

He texts, "YESSSSSS!!!" the hiss of all caps sibilants already running down my spine.

I tease back—cos no way do I believe it—r u gonna send me a plane tix?

Faster than lightspeed, he replies his chauffeur will collect me in NYC on Nov. 1st about 8-ish.

I text that's awesome. *Collect* impresses me. But also brings to mind a butterfly collection: beautiful creatures pinned down. I brush away my silly thought to read his next text.

Rodomontade is odious, he texts, but forgive my humble-brag. Crypto has been good to me and afforded me the luxury of acquiring a Rolls Royce from India, a model called "New Ghost." I am fond of crypt—fond of *crypto trading*. Opportunities 24/7. Enough gasconade, my sweet. *Pana atunci, dragamea*!

Really working Google translate tonight. His words meant: "Until then, my dearest." Guess he has a dreamy foreign accent and that's why his English is...unusual. Before I can reply, he texts 3 heart emojis. I ask if there's a dress code—but it seems he's left me on read cos just dead space follows.

My dorm mate Megan hung a wall calendar with moon phases and holidays. Flipping up the page to see if there's a full moon on the first of November, I notice it's the Catholic holyday Feast of All Saints. The day of the dead.

*Excerpt from "Venus and Madonna" by Romanian poet Mihai Eminescu [1850 - 1889]

Our Version of Events – Simon J. Plant (he/him)

Me and Lila were in trouble that afternoon twenty years ago. I remember it like it was yesterday. "Not again," father growled, standing with his head about to the rafters; my twin sister and I quavering like autumn leaves in his shadow. He passed out punishments with the gruffness of a blackjack dealer—one wearied from serving insatiable addicts all day. We knew this time he would not go easy

"We couldn't help ourselves," I tried to explain, "we're only weeks past our tenth birthday, we don't know any better, we're just kids."

He pointed to the smears covering the kitchen floor and caught himself before speaking. The smell and the stuff dribbling down our chins evoked an unexpected response from his upper digestive tract. He covered his mouth and gagged like the dog used to do when she'd eaten too quickly.

"Clean this up," he said, talking at us like we were one. My sister and I, though badly paired, were a team, no matter what the newspapers claimed. Our version of events is the only one you should believe.

When mother came in from the garden, she was equally outraged. "Jesus Christ!" she riled, hands still dirty from digging in the garden, helping to clean last night's mess. I thought of our sweet-natured babysitter, a young woman who'd only ever meant well, and sighed. *Poor Wendy. She deserved better than to rot in an unmarked grave.* "I can't do this again," said mother, looking like she'd lugged a pile of bricks up a hill to find she had another load to carry. She turned to father and threw her hands in the air, "I can't, John. I won't."

"Come on," whispered Lila to me, eyes sparkling. My sister was a devil. I loved her dearly, but she was a bad influence on me, a naughty girl whose ideas only ever led to trouble. "Let's get cleaned up," she suggested, eyeing our parents with glee, "They look angry…"

"What the hell is wrong with her?" I heard mother say later, her voice from the kitchen finding me through the bathroom wall. Soiled garments hanged like empty sock puppets over the hamper, stains prevalent despite our use of cold water on them. Steam still wafted in the air from our shower.

I felt relieved listening to mother's wails. What's wrong with *her*, she'd said. I'd told them before that Lila was the instigator, that I only went along because it was harder to deny her. Too often they saw us as identical, one identity, one culpability, one troublesome personality.

"When will this end?"

"Tonight," came father's decisive response. He placed what sounded like a shovel upon the kitchen bench and repeated," We end this now."

"You know what that means, don't you?" whispered Lila scandalously, wrapped in a bath towel and dripping wet as she eyed me through the mirror. You'd hardly tell us apart in that moment. The only distinguishable difference was the lack of fear on Lila's face; whereas her eyes were set to defend against naysayers, mine were hooded with dread. "It means he's getting rid of us," she answered herself ominously. Us? I wondered. Just you, I would have told her, but she was adamant: "Both of us."

Into the hall we crept, silently observing our parents from the dark. Mother was hunched like a banshee over the kitchen sink and father, green-faced, looked as if he'd contracted a bug; he snatched the soiled shovel from the bench and propped it in the pantry.

"Where'd you bury it," mother said without looking up. I imagined Lila and me tumbling down the drain before her like miniature toy soldiers and mother flicking on the garbage disposal to be rid of us.

"In the garden," he grumbled." Where do you think?"

"I know *that*," she said impatiently," I meant where—"

"Next to Wendy," he snapped. "Wendy always liked the dog. Now they can be together."

Mother took in a shuddering breath. "Lord help us..."

"He'll take us to the basement again," Lila whispered in my ear, and though she was warning me, her tone was full of mirth. I chided her for it. The cage he sometimes locked us in down there was no joking matter. "Only this time," she added, as if I had not spoken, "there's no escape."

"What do we do, John?" mother said. "How do we handle this?"

"Police," he said heavily. "It's time they knew." I heard something like a growl coming from inside Lila's chest. I looked at mother; justifications clashed like warring countries upon her face, but the prevailing emotion was agreement. She reached for the telephone on the wall.

I could not have stopped Lila from doing what she did next. I'd always been slower than my sister. Lila was a spitfire. She dashed into the kitchen and snatched the shovel from the pantry, the door standing open still, despite mother constantly scorning father's slovenliness. "Were you raised in a barn?" she'd say coquettishly whenever he forgot to latch the side gate or use a coaster. I'm not sure exactly what Lila intended. Maybe to threaten, or to promise she wouldn't do it again. Either way, I don't believe it was this.

Mother turned sharply and it took Lila off guard. Reflex saw her swing the shovel like a baseball bat. The flat side bonked mother upside the head and she fell to the floor. That might have been the worst of it, only, the sound of her temple connecting with the bench corner on the way down was like a dry branch cracking.

I stared in disbelief as blood seeped across the floor and silence filled the room. Then felt a flush of defensiveness as, per usual, my father turned to me. Why me? I thought angrily. *I* didn't do it, it was *her.* I wanted to reach for him, to remind him that I was the good one, his innocent daughter, not the bad seed he'd forever associated me with. But next thing I knew, he was spitting red; the sharp end of the shovel had buried itself in his neck.

"It was self-defense," Lila said later as we dashed through nighttime woodland, "I was protecting you." I could not respond. All I could think of was how, even in death, our father wore that same mask of outrage, that same infuriating accusation, as if me and not Lila had swung the damn shovel. In my reticence, I lost her.

Fleeing into the forest, trees thick as smoke, we were separated. Rage at being perpetually misunderstood by my father is what fueled my survival, warding off discovery the way heavy treads scare snakes from forest paths. When park rangers found me two days later, the newspapers erupted like wildfire. But don't believe everything you read. Authorities might not have bought my claims, but you still can.

They never caught Lila. She was quicker running through those woods than I, more allusive and clever. To this day I don't know what became of her. I hope she reached Canada and changed her identity, and lives peacefully in a cabin on some snowy far-off mountain. Despite everything, I wish her well.

As for me, hard as I tried to explain myself in court, there was only ever one birth certificate to call on—and it was Lila's. You probably know her as Lila the Cannibal, the name they immortalized her with on the nightly news. A thirty-something "disturbed individual" under the delusion she was a ten-year-old girl with a malefic twin sister who'd mysteriously—conveniently—vanished. Her parents took extreme measures in covering up their daughter's crimes; the murder of her long-term psychiatric-carer, not to mention various other incidents I really haven't the time right now to recount.

Patricide put someone they *thought* was Lila away for many years. The murder of Wendy Becker might have added to that sentence had a "plea of insanity" not worked in my favor. The half-eaten dog they found buried in the back garden, along with what remained of poor Wendy, only added to Lila's notoriety as an idol of urban lore.

Nowadays I spend my hours locked in this padded grey cell with people like you ogling me, taking notes, monitoring my words and trying to puzzle out the inner workings of my brain. I shiver with frustrations every time I contemplate my innocence in all this. But it's okay; my patience is vast. Someday soon, Lila will appear again. She will save me. I know she will. It's only a matter of time.

The Ghosts You Call Up – Sarah Crabtree (she/her)

You come downstairs in the morning and the computer screen is already on. Waiting for you. An easy enough explanation: You forgot to switch it off last night; it went into standby; the screen moved from black to blue light because the vibrations of your footsteps were enough to set it in motion. A strong hit of caffeine is needed.

You settle down with your coffee and begin typing. You type his postcode in the search box. You are not really stalking him. Just checking he still lives there. You wonder if either or both his parents are still alive, mentally calculate their rough ages and how they sit against the normal demographic. They seemed healthy and a tad wealthy. Younger than your deceased parents by approximately ten years. So it is likely at least one has survived the statistical threat of disease and accident.

You find more information. The algorithms are working well today. You feel there should be an extra 'i' in that word, but it likely comes from Ancient Greek, and they never wasted letters, you reckon.

You feel a chill at the back of your neck. You rub it and mutter a small 'damn' under your breath. You don't usually talk to yourself, unlike most people who live alone, but you do think you remembered to close the small window in the lounge last night. There has been a spate of break-ins of late. A neighbour's TV was taken in broad daylight. It will be for sale on an online marketplace. Somebody will get a bargain. You also read elsewhere that the local police put unclaimed recovered items on for sale; likewise, airlines sell off lost cases. You wonder if anybody ever buys back their own stuff because they haven't remembered it was theirs to start with.

You pour yourself another black coffee. It's time to log into your office account and make it appear you are doing some real work. There are forty-seven emails awaiting an answer. Each is more urgent than the previous one. A number are repeated enquiries: Why didn't you respond to my email from last week? Now the customer is wondering if we are actually doing something. The customer is angry now. The customer wants answers.

You open another window and check your bank account to see if you have been paid. The amount is smaller than you expected. Did they type in the wrong tax code? You scribble a note on a yellow pad to remind yourself to send an email to HR.

Your neck feels stiff. You remove your fingers from the keyboard and rub that bone at the back; the place equidistant between your shoulders. There. That's better. It's time for another coffee top-up. A cafetiere. You should try decaffeinated next time. You will make a note and think about it.

After half an hour's more typing, more emails come in: That's not a good enough answer! Yet it was an answer all the same. Most of your emails in your inbox won't get the courtesy of a reply. So there. You want to type that cheeky message, but you won't because it will only cause more moaning from middle management. And you really hate it when middle management moans, despite you knowing deep down that is what middle management's purpose is—to moan at those further down in the pecking order. Good one. You smirk, then bite into a ginger biscuit.

You google his surname, and it comes up with several people bearing his name. There is a way you can search and cover your tracks, but where is the fun in that, eh? You bite into another ginger biscuit. The crumbs tumble off your lap and onto the wooden floor. You don't care. You are getting somewhere now. His parents have done the savvy thing and registered their home as a business. To avoid having to pay care home costs. That was sneaky of them. You remember the way he always managed to stay in and out of the crowd. He eavesdropped and partially joined in on the gossip. You believe he might even have been behind that rumour you ran away from home for a bit. There again, what would he have achieved by doing that? It's not as if you were both competing for the same place in a firm or university. It's not as if he wanted to get one over you for some reason.

And there's more. He filed a complaint about a pothole in his road. He lives in the countryside, so what does he expect? A Smart motorway? Again, you smirk at your wit. You are being paid to be a total sneak, and nobody knows anything about it. Except, if he is a whiz on computers, he will already have rumbled you.

You rather like the idea of that. In fact, when you nip into town, you think you spot his old friend from school. The gormless one he sat with on the bus. You are sure it is him. Like you, he is bundled up against the weather, but he gives you that sideways look you remember from way back. That look that is a look but isn't really a look because by the time you have realised he was checking you out, he has snuck across the road into the pub.

Then you are sure they are onto you when you go into the newsagent. The main guy is already there, waiting by the greetings cards. He picks up a Mother's Day card, pretends to look at it, slots it back into its wooden holder, and then walks out through the swing doors; all the while doing that sideways look that tells you he spotted you but didn't really acknowledge he spotted you.

It would be infuriating if you really cared after all these years. What is their game? you wonder. Is it because they caught you snooping? Do they think you are trying to catch them out? Are they avoiding paying tax? Are they giving you a silent warning: Lay off. We know you're snooping.

What will they do if you don't stop? You are only an old ghost from the past who managed to call herself up, and somehow, you got caught in their machine's headlights. It can't hurt. You mean no harm.

You are sure you shut that window last night. You convince yourself somebody has been inside your house. He or they, as maybe it was two of them, managed to let themselves in; they switched on your computer; they read your files; they found it stuffy in here, so they opened the skylight to let in some fresh air. They got all the information they needed. They left without remembering to close the skylight. Should you ring the police?

Hello?

Madam?

I think somebody broke into my house while I was sleeping.

Did they take anything?

I don't think so.

A pause. You think you hear a sigh. They think you are a time-waster. They get lots of those. Some people tap in the three nines if their take-away doesn't arrive on time. You begin to worry you are going to get into trouble for wasting police time. Should you try to justify your concerns? Should you hang up? Should you apologise? No, definitely don't say you are sorry. You are sure now that somebody has been into your house and stolen something. Not something tangible, but a piece of information about you. Something private. You don't know what. It could be anything. It might be one piece of private information. Or it might be a number of pieces of information. There are photos on your computer. There are poems you have penned. They might have some algorithmic proof, if there is such a word, that you have been stalking them on and off for over thirty years. They might know that in your head you have been living an alternative existence. That you dreamed something about the main man. They might be able to call up that dream on their computer and play it to all those people you used to hang out with. All those people you sort-of fell out with because you might have teased them about a boy. Yes, you remember now. Somebody told you about a party where a girl got off with a boy, and you laughed about it. You didn't think the gossip would shop you, but she did, didn't she? And how do you know that? Because years later you were at some Xmas bash, and some old, school chums turned up, and one of them had a dig at you about a date and how you were actually with a date, like it was some huge deal. That was when you knew that your response had been fed back to this person, and it had hurt her so badly that after all this time, she took the one chance that was afforded to her to make you feel like a fool.

Should you feel a need to apologise for being so catty? Maybe the person who told you that information had a crush on the boy and was jealous her friend managed to get him into a clinch instead of her. You weren't even at the party, so you could only rely on what was being told you. People lie when they have too much to drink. It wasn't as if there was Facebook or smartphones then. It's not as if it could have been recorded and played back.

Yet, if it's all still in your memory banks, then there is a record of it. Somebody who has the knowledge can log into your brain and access that information.

They know, you tell the policeman. "They know all my thoughts. They have stolen them, and I want them back before it's too late."

The policeman sighs again, then says in the tone of a voice addressing a child: Is there somebody you can call, love? Somebody who can stay with you tonight?

He is a policeman plod, you decide. He doesn't get it. It's not his fault. This is way above his pay grade. It's all the cutbacks, see. They don't have the manpower to put enough boots on the streets, let alone train their officers in the complexities of dealing with those criminals who steal people's thoughts.

Been reading too much Orwell, have you, love?

Now he's taking the mick. You mutter a farewell and hang up.

As far as you are concerned, that is the end of the matter. Your call will have been logged along with all the other nutcases he has had to deal with while on duty. Off duty, he might share a pint with a mate and have a laugh over yet another one that needs locking up.

Your mouth is dry and your smartphone is flashing. Middle management wants to speak to you about something somebody else has messed up. The word 'scapegoat' enters your mind. You let the call shift to voicemail. There are now so many messages on your phone that it has reached tipping point. Good. The battery is almost out of gas. Even better.

You press 'send and receive.' More emails. More complaints. You have been reminded time and time again not to open attachments. You are so tanked up with caffeine that you don't care. The attachment opens and plays out a memory.

One memory you thought had been buried for ever.

How can this be?

It is a summary of the worst parts of your life:

The lies, the cheating, the snooping: Hiding in doorways, staring, looking through drawers, watching couples through their lounge windows.

All this time you never realised what a creep you are.

As the clip comes to its miserable close, you hear the doorbell ring. You ignore it. It rings again. You lose count of how many times it rings because it Never. Stops. Ringing.

The Peshaman Fragments – Greg Sendi (he/him)

Following the highly publicized disappearance of Elias Peshaman late last year, this unfinished manuscript was discovered among a small number of uncurated cloud files authorities reviewed for information related to his whereabouts. For more than a decade, Monsieur Peshaman served the Société Gaspardine Defaux as its VQ Section Editor and became an indispensable contributor of new thinking within our field. Intrigued by these fragments, the General Secretariat has made the decision, in consultation with his family, to publish them in their current form and has requested that interested readers share their thoughts with the Société as to their interpretation, especially as may regard his disappearance and the nature of what he believed to have discovered at or near the time he vanished. While we continue to hope for M. Peshaman's safe return and eventual completion of his own manuscript, we are mindful of the importance of sharing the information we have, a decision Peshaman would, we think, have supported. Readers with contributions to make, either to the question of his whereabouts or the findings presented in these fragments, are invited to contact the Société Gaspardine Defaux at laffairePeshaman@socgaspdef.org or via the posted link at the Société's website.

FRAGMENT 1

It is a mouth radically different from other human mouths—infused with an eerie otherworldliness. The mouth attracts attention precisely because of its unsettling difference. It seizes the attention of others because, like a catastrophic car accident, we can't look away. To some, this mouth is hyper-real and in its weird fleshiness, suggests an authenticity, the way a blood-rare steak suggests "real food."

When at rest, the mouth often does not relax but returns to a puckered, circular kissing shape that suggests it is at once both open and closed, an

300

orifice of both inbound and outbound potential. Let's be honest, this mouth also has an anal quality to it and is always pantomiming an expulsion of waste. It is always conveying the ejection of impurity, mirroring his promises to eject things and people.

There is also the tongue. Disabled by the neuro-impairments that prevent its full control, the tongue throbs, bends, and extrudes in ways that reinforce the expulsion conveyed by the lips.

In its totality, the shape of the mouth as an emblem of disgust and discharge is also connected to his frequent interest in what comes out of human bodies, especially the bodies of women. It enacts his revulsion at excretion, for example, or menstruation or breast feeding.

FRAGMENT 2

altogether ill at ease about what is happening with us

FRAGMENT 3

The water hyacinth (*Eichhornia crassipes*) is a large aquatic plant native to the Amazon basin. It is known chiefly for its ability to overwhelm the surface of bodies of water, pushing out native species and depleting its water ecosystem of oxygen, suffocating all fish, water creatures and other plants.

So too, all the things he is—liar, chiseler, malignant degenerate, traitor, deadbeat, daughterfucker wannabe, child rapist—may be viewed as precisely evolved for indifference to the question of what a "pond," is actually for. The old blackhats (Ratched, Moriarty) are quaint by comparison.

FRAGMENT 5

His skin, like the fixtures around him, in the primitive way imaginable, conveys that he cannot escape how gold rushes in upon him, following him like a cloud of gold dust seeking the man who is both its source and its destination. He is Chrysos, Xipe Totec, Midas, Shen Wanshan, Goldfinger, communicating with every image not that, "I'm like my people," but rather, "I'm radically unlike my people or any people."

But in its obvious artificiality there is more. With his skin, he is sending us a message deeper than, "I am a golden man." The message also says, "I am wearing a me-shaped golden suit." His skin invites you to imagine an inner creature, but simultaneously humiliates you for accepting the invitation.

To some, the skin is an alarm light alerting to a dangerous duplicity—the way the coloration of certain animals alerts other animals not to eat them. To others, the situation is more complex. Via its alchemy, broadly speaking, there can be a gratitude, even a love, engendered by the ways he affirms the fundamental duplicity, and the inevitability of the way things are.

The skin serves both as camouflage (allowing him to blend in with the other perceived liars—like certain poisonous toads blend in with a pile of leaves in the forest) and as a beacon calling attention to itself as

302

camouflage (providing a basis of assurance and trust—as if he might be the one true leaf in a pile of poisonous toads).

FRAGMENT 6

Read marcus aurelius, of each particular thing ask what is it in itself, what is its nature, what does he do, this man you seek

FRAGMENT 7

In totality, we know this as "The Uncanny Valley," a term coined by Japanese roboticist Masahiro Mori to describe the phenomenon by which robots become deeply disconcerting to us at the point where they come closest to mimicking human features.

The Uncanny Valley teaches us to think about how we are different (if we are) and how we are the same (if we are). Perhaps it teaches an instinctive revulsion at the not-quite-human—an instinct that may have prevented our early ancestors from breeding with apes. Though perhaps also (if not instead), it teaches us revulsion at ourselves, at what we are capable of. Perhaps it forces us to ask: When face to face with a monster masquerading as your companion, what do you do?

Mirroring the nausea created by our experience, his experience as a sociopath may be one of looking at us across his Uncanny Valley, where he is unable to see or feel the full humanity of any person—to distinguish emotionally between a chair, a car, a bucket, a fish or child. To operate across his Valley, he creates simulacra of human engagement to deal with people because he is unable to generate actual human responses.

Little by little as he deprives our pond of oxygen, he becomes less able to conceal the fact that when he looks at us, no matter who we are, he sees the same lifeless mask we see when we look at him, useful to him or useless, using our own shames and weaknesses and hatreds against us the way a serial killer might use the skin of his victim to make a lampshade.

FRAGMENT 8

my god my god to be haunted by the end of everything we are and have created together it is like choking finally after all it will be like choking my god they are gouging his eyes with a flagpole i think

Here Peshaman's manuscript ends, providing scant basis for development of a general synthesis. While the Société Gaspardine Defaux is pleased to share this important manuscript with specialist and lay audiences, overall, we urge caution in the extrapolation of broad-brush conclusions from what was clearly a work left unfinished and in disarray at the time of his disappearance.

Magic Palm – Kevin Brown (he/him)

An angel, Grandmother would say, saved her life during a four-story suicide jump the year China went Red. Me on her lap, she told how she toed the ledge, stared out at the network of alleyways smothered in smoke and screams and men tearing through men. How she leaned forward and the landscape fell up, toward and past her. How Kuan Shih Yin, the Goddess of Mercy, appeared and placed a palm beneath her. Whispered, "The Earth shall keep spinning. Spin with it," and eased her to the ground. "I broke a leg and both arms," she said, raising two gnarled fingers, "but it was magical."

I'd cry when she told me about Grandfather, whom she hadn't seen since the day he was taken away. He'd been a politician in the Nationalist Government, and so imprisoned for life. "They took my possessions," she said, "then my husband. Forced me to bow and confess against him to avoid his immediate execution." She'd stare ahead. "Last time I heard his voice, he was screaming mine and your mother's names as they drug him away." She'd blink several times and I could see the image dissipating, melting into the now. "We were helpless in a country that needed help," she said. "Unable to save those who needed saving."

Years later, we returned to the location of her old house, but it was gone, replaced by an office building. Grandmother only smiled and said, "Prettier than it used to be."

She died shortly after. As she was lowered into the ground, I asked Mother if she believed a Deva really saved her.

"I don't *not* believe it," Mother said.

I was married later that year, and each time I looked at my husband, I'd think of Grandmother's story. How hard it must've been to have everything one second and be bowing as it is dragged away the next. How easy it'd be to jump. How hard to climb down.

305

So, I mentally recorded my husband's voice, his smells. Behind my eyes, I imprinted his shape and face. Then, on June 4th, 1989, he was killed in Tiananmen Square, when a tank rolled between us and has never moved since.

A week later, I stood on my own four-story ledge with a bottle of prescription pills. Toed the edge and looked out at my mental vision of the world, a network of alleyways that all led to the same dead end. At everyone helpless in a country that needed help. I missed my husband. Wanted to see Grandmother arm-in-arm with Grandfather, the memories of forced bows and screams erased forever. So I jumped by swallowing every pill. Felt the landscape fall up, toward and past me, until my angel, my Goddess of Mercy, my grandmother appeared, and placed a withered palm beneath me.

Whispered: "The world shall keep spinning. Spin with it," and eased me to the ground, where I vomited, and it was magical.

The Chair – Rachel Rose (she/her)

When my mom found out that I was moving to Illinois, to an unfurnished apartment no less, she immediately went to the K-Mart to buy me furniture. Obviously anything bought at home in Texas would be far superior to and cheaper than anything purchased in "good-for-nothing Yankeeland". Amid her bounty was a smallish, circular kitchen table and four bronze metal chairs with tan cushions. This rather non-descript set from an all but gone business has followed me these past five years from apartment to apartment without comment or complaint.

The cheap wooden tabletop is often pretentiously bedecked with a seasonal tablecloth bearing the stains of my cooking triumphs and failures. At times it has supported creative place settings with delicious meals. More often than not, it has rather humbly supported my sneakers, dishes from three days ago, or all of the unfolded laundry.

And what can I say for the chairs? Their cushions have hosted and supported the butts of innumerable friends, while their lattice-work backs have so often supported my coat or a shopping bag. Although more commonly recognized for their comfort-enhancing abilities, these chairs have also served me well as a ladder to hang a picture or turn off the fire alarm.

These items have performed their duties well both individually and as a unit in their intended and unintended uses. However, there is one chair which has become the elephant in the room. Locked away in the dungeon of my crafting and storage space, it rarely sees the light of day. I try not to think about that chair too often. I'm sure it feels the injustice of having served its mistress in her greatest hour of need and then being punished for the battle scars it now displays. From time to time, I do enter this space of all lost and unwanted objects, the "black hole room" my boyfriend calls it, for this ball of yarn or that paintbrush. Now that I am packing to move, the frequency has increased. I see the chair in the corner and yet again internalize the dilemma of what to do with it.

"Could it be repaired?" I ask.

"No," my boyfriend tells me frankly. "The metal bar is bent in and completely broken. You would need a welder or something. It's not worth it." He is unaware of the history of the chair.

I then resort to anthropomorphizing the chair.

"But if I get rid of it, then I will only have three chairs. It is part of the set. The other chairs will miss it, and it will miss them."

This is a very ridiculous line of reasoning, but it has allowed me to keep the chair.

I spent a lot of time not thinking about the chair. Not thinking about how it looked, or why it looked the way it looked. A lot of time not entertaining the related memories. I tried not to think about how my mom had used the chair as a brace against the door so that my husband couldn't get into the apartment after I told him I was leaving him.

"It's just so he can't sneak in without us knowing about it," she told me reassuringly in that way moms do.

I also try not to think about how the next morning I was awakened from a night of crying by the enormous bang of my husband forcing the door open and running to the bed my mom and I were sharing, crying and begging me, "Don't do this to me!" When I rose from the bed, he fell to his knees and began to cry and beg. He grabbed my wrists and wouldn't let me move.

My mom called my dad, working five states away, and asked him what to do. First, he told us that I should get dressed and go to work. It was the safest place for me at the moment.

When I rose from the bed and started dressing, he was still crying and begging. He wouldn't let go of my wrists and wouldn't let me move or put clothes on.

"Let me speak to him," I heard my dad say, his normally gentle voice gruff and stern with anger.

My mom gave my still crying husband the phone, and he released me for now.

My dad spoke to him petulantly, patronizingly, almost as though to a child, "You have to let my daughter go. I am afraid you are going to hit my daughter."

"No!" the thirty-two-year-old man-child wailed.

He was watching me put my clothes on. First my bra, then a shirt, and finally pants. I felt his eyes surveying my nakedness, but I would not look at him.

"Are you doing drugs?" my dad asked him calmly. "She says you don't spend very much time in the home and want to control her money."

"No!" this person once so close to me wailed again. "I love her. I don't know why she is doing this to me. You have to believe me."

Now he was running after me as I walked to my car.

"Are you having an affair? Why are you never at home?" my father asked him again.

"No! I would never cheat on her. I love her!" my husband said.

Now he was standing in front of the car. I turned the handle to open the door, and he slammed the door closed with his body.

"You have to let me go," I told him quietly.

And eventually he let me go.

This chair and I share so many scars from living with that man. My scars cannot be seen, but the chair was not so lucky. When he forced the door open, he had pushed the chair to its very limit. It tried so hard to hold him off, but it failed, showing all the signs of wear and tear for its attempt.

I am not the chair. I can heal and move on. For that reason, the chair had to go.

I put it outside by the dumpster, and within an hour it was gone. I am sure someone in my apartment complex saw this perfectly good chair and judged the person who would dump something for minimal imperfection.

It is the sort of thing I would have thought in that situation, "It still sits just fine! Why get rid of a perfectly good chair?"

After the chair was gone, I realized that something had changed. I never not-thought about the chair at all. In fact, the only time I thought about the chair, was to realize how much time I had spent not thinking about it before. The burden of that chair has been lifted from me.

In my new life, in my new apartment, a fourth chair would have been one too many.

I had to eventually let it go.

Las Sinverguenzas (The Shameless Girls) – B. Lynn Carter (she/her)

It doesn't hurt them anymore. The girls can hardly recall that torturous sensation, tiny glass-like crystals biting into their flesh. They never even noticed exactly when the pain subsided. It was so gradual. The bloody, open sores on their skinned elbows had turned to scabs and the scabs had turned to calluses, cushions against the ravishes of the jagged gravel and concrete window ledge.

The two cousins, lean out as far as they dare resting numb elbows on the ledge, balancing heads on fists beneath their chins. This is how they pass all of their days, watching all the boys and girls playing on the street below.

They know all the games. From their first-floor vantage point, they see and hear all that goes on. Layla loves when they play "Johnny On The Pony." The attacking team takes a running leap and flies through the air, landing on the defending teams' bent backs. The defenders try not to collapse under the weight of the assault before the "words" can be said three times: "Johnny on the pony, one, two, three! Johnny on the pony, one, two, three! Johnny on the pony, one, two, three!" Then they all fall down in a delightful heap of confusion and laughter. Layla imagines herself flying through the air and landing on bent backs with a thud. She can almost feel the wind on her face and breeze through her hair as she flies.

Her younger cousin Ana gushes about how she would love to play "Three Feet to Germany." A game that was made-up on the block. She watches intently as the one who is "It" calls, "Three feet to Germany, all aboard!" She imagines leaping into the street, with three long graceful strides. Then, she'd turn and twist, fake and dodge, and get to the other side without ever being tackled.

The girls know all the players. As she often does, Layla sits counting them off in her head. There's Orlando who attends St Johns with them. He's cute, with his black curly hair and smooth brown skin. There's Hector "Cavy-Baby" the caveman and his younger brother

311

Edwin who Ana can't take her eyes off. There's Margie known for her "fabulous fanny." Millie the princess, the colored kids, Laney and Karlzy, DeeDee blue eyes and her brother Tony.

Then there's Little Corine, the white girl who lives with her father. Rumor has it that her mother ran away but Layla believes that her mother only died. Having your mother die is much better than having her just leave. Mothers who just leave are somewhere, without you, living a life, probably happy—far away from Octăvia.

***

Octăvia, for her part, has been ruminating about the girls, all day. She's sure they are up to something. She's had experience with raising girls and none of it has been good.

Today, all day, she's been pacing back and forth over the short length of the kitchen floor. She sits at her kitchen table and mumbles over cups of hot cafe Bustello con leche, *Girls! They are the spawn of the devil. Why hadn't God blessed me with sons instead of daughters? And now, these granddaughters to raise,* she thinks, addressing her thoughts to the aromatic coffee steaming in her cup. *But it's not really their fault. It's not like they can control themselves,* she muses, rises, resumes her pacing. *It's in their nature. It's the way girls are. It's written in the Bible; right? Didn't Eve tempt Adam and drag us all into a world of sin?*

Exhausted, Octăvia decides to rest her head on the table for just a moment. Soon, she finds herself tumbling into a familiar dream.

He is mist, a shimmering figure, an apparition, shrouded in fog. He floats into her darkened bedroom...again. She cannot make out his face, but she knows; yes. she knows exactly who he is, who she wants him to be. Now, she is not frightened, not anymore. Pushing aside her Teddy bear, she tosses her hair and licks her lips in an attempt to be seductive. She tingles with expectation and the delicious anxiety that comes with the forbidden. Mamá is asleep. She sweeps aside a tinge of guilt that threatens to spoil her pleasure. It dissipates into the fog. She feels her body responding. It feels so good, so very good.

But then, he is morphing. His body is solidifying, is no longer soft gentle mist. He is growing bigger, harder, as she begins to shrink. She is getting smaller and smaller. He is getting heavier, and heavier, so heavy! She is being crushed, smothered. Gasping for air, her screams are stifled under his girth. She cannot breathe, can't scream, can't scream!!!

Octăvia's head jerks upright. Silent screams leave her struggling for air. Trembling, she uses the kitchen towel to wipe cold sweat from her face and neck as the details of the wicked dream dissipate and ebb away, leaving only vague intermingled feelings of pleasure and . dread.

Although she cannot remember exactly what happened in the dream, she knows this is the same dream that had haunted her for years in her youth. Now, for some reason, it is back.

This is a sign, she shoots thoughts at the kitchen walls as she prepares the arroz con pollo. *Something to do with them girls.* She strains, willing the dream to reveal its meaning. Clearly, she needs to do more to protect those girls, not so much, from the males who would prey upon them, but from their own natural base instincts to invite that attention. Such is the nature of girls.

Octăvia paces, wrestles with her thoughts, the disturbing dream, the need to stay vigilant with those girls.

Where had she gone wrong with her own two daughters? She had watched them like a hawk, but their capacity for sneakiness proved to be akin to genius. Perhaps she should've started monitoring their activities at an earlier age, like her own dear Mamá had done with her. Then feeling suddenly flustered, Octăvia takes a breath and realigns her thoughts. *But with Mamá, that was a different situation altogether. Here in this country there are so many ways that young girls can get "nasty, indecent" ideas, so many opportunities for them to act on them.*

The television for one, she muses, turning to the pot of kidney beans bubbling on the stove, the savory fragrance winging through the air. Cutting out television was a real good move. But now, they're always looking out that window at those kids out there doing those nasty, indecent things, right out there in the open! I can't believe how shameless those girls out there are!

The doorbell is ringing. They are home.

***

Like most days, when the girls get home from school they stop outside their apartment door to tie back their long flowing hair, wipe the tinted lip gloss from their lips and roll down their uniform skirts.

"Octăvia, bendición," they call, asking for their grandmother's blessing as is the custom in their Puerto Rican household.

"Dios te vendiga," she replies, bestowing God's blessing upon them.

As always, they are greeted by the sumptuous smells of Octăvia's cooking. As always, Octăvia stands before them, a large imposing figure reminiscent of a heavy-set Mongolian woman. Her thin, straight hair pulled up into a severe bun at the top of her head, meaty arms crossed. Each girl hands over her book bag. They stand there while, seeking evidence of impending lechery, Octăvia inspects every page of every book and every pocket of each bag.

On most days, the girls would do their homework and head for the window. But on this day Octăvia stops them.

"I don wan ju luuking at dose muchachas indicentes, dose nasty Sinverguezas!" she rails. "Out dere playin wit boys. Das nasty!" She

314

pauses to let her meaning sink in, enjoying the devastated looks on their faces. "Dos girls dey gonna eend up prenant for sure!!"

"Last time Momi came, she said it was okay to look out the window," Layla cries

"Mine too," comes a plead from Ana.

"Ju moother? Ju moother?" she shrieks "¿Donde estan? She says taunting the girls, knowing they have no idea where their respective mothers are. "Dats eszackly wat happin to ju moother!! Dey waz muchachas indicentes; sinverguenzas!"

Having previously felt the sting of Octăvia's heavy hand, across their faces, the girls swallow the urge to argue, chancing only a slight pout and a shuffling of their feet, they retreat to their room.

***

Now, the girls spend all their time in their room speculating about what the "sinverguenzas" might be doing outside. Before, Layla had never really understood what was going on out there, had no idea. She thought it was only kids playing games and having fun with friends. But now, she realizes that Octăvia's adult eyes see the truth. Johnny on the Pony is cleverly disguised as a game. Octăvia says it's nasty. Replaying it in her head, Layla visualizes the girls bent over, their young backsides held high, seductively, invitingly. The boys, say the words three times before succumbing to their "nastiness." Then they all collapse, rubbing, touching and grabbing. It's like that TV show they saw once, before Octăvia said no more TV because TV's "nasty." Layla never quite understood the nature of "nasty." What qualified as "nasty?" When Layla shared her new insights about the games with her little cousin, Ana also began to consider the nature of the "nastiness."

Now, that they understand about the games, new feelings are taking root in them, feelings they'd never felt before, strange tingly feelings, like urges, like desires. It's true that they had always longed to do what the kids outside were doing, but now, now even more so.

Standing nude in front of the full-length mirror, Layla combs her long, dark hair and wonders if those "nasty" boys would like to touch her too. *What would it feel like?* Ana imagines kissing her capturer in the game, his hands exploring her thighs. At night Layla's hands make their way between her legs. *Is this "nasty?"*

After a while the girls start sneaking to the window when Octǎvia is taking her afternoon nap. Then, when they can stand it no longer, they resolve to make a plan.

***

Staring into her contorting face, the girls watch Octǎvia as she twists and turns. She moans and mumbles. Octǎvia is sleeping. The Sun is setting. The time is perfect. With their hearts beating with fear as well as anticipation, they slip out the door. They find the group of girls and boys sitting on the front stoop planning their next adventure, no doubt. Surprised to see them, Orlando starts to speak but Layla hushes him with a delicate finger to his lips followed by a kiss placed ever so lightly. With his eyes wide, his face registering shock, she takes him by the hand and leads him into the building's closed doors. Following her big cousin's lead, Ana grabs the bewildered Edwin and does the same.

"Is that those girls, the ones who look out the window all the time?" asks Laney

"Yeah," from Hector, "What the hell are they doing?"

"Ay que sinverguenzas!" Margie howls, smirking.

Across the street an imposing figure peers out of an apartment building's first-floor window. Leaning on calloused elbows that feel no sensation, Octǎvia stares blankly as tears roll down her face.

On My Own – Marija Rakić Mimica (she/her)
—*Translated by Tatjana Radmilo*

"Fuck, why?" my mother screamed when I told her for the first time that I was leaving my husband.

I'm not happy, how's that for a reason.

She was sitting on the sofa, her hair a mess, dressed in a white robe with a cigarette in her hand, constantly scratching her face in a nervous way, like an allergic puppy.

"How are you going to survive on your own?" she looked at me as if I told her that I intended to travel to Mars on my own, in a laboratory-manufactured jet aircraft.

I don't know. Fuck it, I don't know how I'm going to survive on my own.

Hell, I don't understand what it is with pushing the concept of women's independence and then troubling us with the idea that we have to handle all life situations without anybody's help. For one thing, I don't know how to top up oil in my car on my own. Once I made a mistake: as I was nervously pulling out a dipstick and putting it back, looking for markings for minimum and maximum, I was wiping it with a cloth and oil dropped all over the engine. Or wherever. I don't know car parts and I don't plan to know them. Later, while I was driving, I was waiting in panic for the smoke to start rising form under the hood, which I barely know how to lift up; last time I tried to do it, something got stuck, and then I hysterically pulled it up and down until I forced it to open. Then I gaped at the engine with no comprehension. Since then, I just kindly ask a gentleman at a service station to check my oil, water, and tyre pressure, I pay him and go in peace. Why should I do everything myself? There are people from different walks of life, I do too many things myself anyway, in addition to raising a six-year-old girl starting school in September.

I'm not afraid of loneliness. I'm scared of the time that is ahead of me: shock reflected in confusion and real physical pain I feel because I've lost my partner (which I could compare to his Godforbid! death), anger and pangs of conscience, that I try to hide away from my child by acting as a monkey with a wide, unnatural smile whenever I see her, meanwhile, I cry as I wash my face in the morning or most often when I'm in the car, so I'm actually making an effort, as my psychiatrist says, to channel my emotions in a meaningful direction. I'm scared of anxiety and panic attacks which incapacitate me for daily activities, leaving me walking around my apartment as a frightened roe deer, my mind focusing on things, such as where I'm going to live to how I'm going to pay new rental and cover monthly overheads, purchase of a new car because the current one is on the death bed, just like my marriage.

I'm lying. Most of all, I'm scared of the time after I submit request for mandatory consultation of spouses to the Social Welfare Centre. After that, I'll be waiting for their summons while thousands of thriller scenarios with elements of horror will be going on in my mind: a socialist room with rotting and damaged brown furniture, my spouse and I sitting on wooden battered chairs, waiting for a blonde lady, her hair tied up in a casual bun and her red glasses perched on top of her nose, to acquaint us with legal, psychological and social consequences of divorce, the importance of child's welfare when such a decision is adopted and preparation of joint parental custody plan. She's going to tell us all about it, she'll help us to learn everything. Without looking us straight in the eyes once.

***

"Have you thought about what you want to do with your life?" Zoran's question caused in me a sensation similar to that when I teach a new lesson and accidentally scratch the board with my nail, making my arms and legs shivery and goose-skinned.

No. I've no idea what I want from my life. I'm even surprised that I know what I don't want. I don't want to be married. I don't want to be a part of this legally and socially arranged union of two people, imposing on me rights and obligations, I don't want to comply with socially conditioned need to "belong" to somebody and thus regulate my sexual and biological drives all for a would-be feeling of

318

security. I haven't planned or imagined my future in this way, in my naive twenties I had no idea what it meant to live with a man, to have a child, to raise it with compromises, or how co-existence with somebody's virtues and faults or everyday consideration of somebody's shortcomings and constant attempts at preservation and nurturing of love looked. And finally brutal realization that all you have shared for years with somebody, closest to you in this rotten world, just collapses and is no more. Not suddenly, but gradually the desire to correct all the things bothering you when it comes to his behaviour, habits, or life energy that you fell in love with, and later sucked out all your energy until the only thing left for you is to run away. So, I ran away, killed it all in a single blow.

"All right, we'll talk about it," I lie to him now, just as I've been lying to myself for the last two years. This is just a common marital crisis, I hear the voices in my head, I had so many sessions of psychotherapy on my own, making hysterical sobbing, wiping my nose, and loud swearing while behind the wheel of my car, a wonderful routine. You talk to yourself; nobody bothers you and nobody pretends to listen to you.

"You're lying," he said and put down the phone.

***

Although I proposed to go our separate ways amicably in order to end the divorce proceedings farce as soon as possible, Zoran didn't agree with Ema living with me and seeing him on a regular basis, so he filed a suit, supplementing it with a report on mandatory consultation, not older than six months and proof of participation at the first family mediation meeting. Mediation at the Social Welfare Centre, preceding the divorce was worse than I had imagined it: the lady neither had a bun nor red glasses, but an austere and thin face with no visible traces of a smile, and her role was to try to improve communication between the spouses in order for us to jointly analyse how and when the problems had occurred and which causes had led to our separation, to acquaint us with legal, psychological and social consequences of the divorce. Yada yada yada. Zoran was sitting next to me, without talking to or looking at me even once, and the lady was addressing him much more often than me because he was mostly giving moral lectures and monologues on my infidelity and not respecting the man, that I, rightly said, had chosen for myself. He was talking to such excess that at one moment I just decided to keep quiet and observe a vein on his forehead, looking like a gossamer thread, becoming more and more visible as he was getting upset while talking that he couldn't have come to any kind of agreement with me because I hadn't wanted to accept any of his proposals, I wanted Ema only for myself and I wasn't giving him a chance to be a father to his girl.

I can't stand monologues and bloody gossamers on his forehead. I stopped talking again: at that moment, when I finally decided to leave, I still kept silent as he continued with preaching from his honourable altar and calling for mediation because I didn't want Ema moving every week, I wanted her to have a home. I didn't plan to forbid her seeing her father, I was not a demon, as he presented the image of me to these outsiders, who had been included into our intimate circle by pure chance and had no feelings for us, for the breakup of our love and fear of my girl, who currently didn't know whether she would live with Mom or Dad. You ego-tripping male, I've just fallen out of love and am taking care of my child.

***

I went through mediation at the Croatian Mediation Association, the famous one that was conducted out of the Social Welfare Centre, and in which the role of mediator was allegedly irreplaceable, while if you asked me, I would gladly replace the lady nodding her head at every word of my soon to be ex-husband, and ignoring me because I had no respect for the father figure and just waiting for the two of us to come to an agreement so that she could go and have a cigarette in the kitchenette, holding it in her manicured and bony fingers, as she closed on yet another case, with any other human being having a little piece of heart and soul. I would like her to stop for a moment and ask us how and where did our love disappear. Somewhere along the way, I would say to her, between romance killing routine and mid-life crisis.

During my divorce proceedings, I pretended to be a human being in front of my child: crying mostly in the toilet or in the car, cursing her father's mother only when she was not around me, loudly wondering at my stupidity and naivete only in solitude, for a while, I was officially and seriously a damaged woman. After summer holidays, Zoran gave up on his request for shared custody; due to unknown reasons, Ema's welfare, I guess, somehow became irrelevant when he realized what it meant to live with a child on his own. He offered me cash payment for the apartment we had lived in and all joint investments in property, that he had inherited from his parents, and a new modern car that we had bought six months before I left in order to travel over Europe during winter school holidays.

Although after twelve years, I finally bought two-tiered red and white curtains for the living room and refurbished most of the rooms with lighter shades and more modern furniture, I didn't stay in that apartment much longer. Some mornings, before going to work, I would have coffee on the balcony, that I completely adapted to myself, and in each sip I would feel the taste of our life that was, when I always poured coffee in two cups, and the cherry tree in our neighbour's garden suddenly became so small and thin, as if it had never spread its kitsch crown into our apartment.

I decided to by a new apartment during the second semester of Ema's fourth grade, when we decided that we didn't want to live in the suburbs anymore, so we would look at several apartments a week in the city centre and looked forward to each new apartment as if it would be our home. We decided to buy a forty meters square apartment in Bačvice. During moving, when I was pulling out a box with our things from one of the last lorries, I saw a neighbour on the balcony next to ours, waving at me and smiling with distrust.

"Neighbour, are you going to carry it up all on your own?" she cried out, leaning over the rail, while her false, homemade perm suddenly vibrated.

"Yes, I am", I said and smiled to my girl, holding the entrance door to the building for me.

You Know I Am No Good – Nelly Shulman (she/her)

I do not know why I have such a fancy for this little café.

The sparse copper burners exude marginal warmth, failing to penetrate the numbing iciness of the wintry city. The sharp wind whips the pedestrians, hurdling them into the corner holes such as the one I have been frequenting lately. The central, brightly lit places swarm with beautiful young things. They order fancy coffees unheard of here, where the dilapidated plaster walls shed the greying particles as if the unkempt man scratches his head, spraying the dandruff pieces around.

Such one usually sits diagonally from me, engrossed in the yellowing paperback with a once bright but now dulling cover, where some monster rips apart the human flesh. I come to the little café every day. He appears here thrice a week, in the late morning. The coffee machine hisses like a sated beast, and the lone waiter in the long black apron takes his time bringing the order, shuffling on his arthritic legs, discontentedly muttering something under his breath.

I imagine him as a poor relative of the café's owner, a smooth, stocky guy with a haughty demeanor. He comes on the new moped, too slim for his ample frame, when the narrow street still drowns in the fog, when the café serves builder's tea and full fry-up. The working people eat quickly before hurrying to their day jobs.

The church bells ring seven. The hoarse voice cuts through the January cold, calling all faithful to the prayer. The gigantic mosque reigns over this area, where the border, dividing the city, runs through the ruined houses and abandoned gardens, overgrown with thistle. Only stray cats cross it easily. All others have to go through the official control post not far from here.

The owner pokes around the café for an hour or so, busying himself. Finally, the wheels of the moped jump up and down on the wet cobblestones. He disappears around the corner, where the dog barks. The bells chime ten, and I order another small cup of coffee.

I see the dog walker in a moment. He never stops at the café, merely passing by the dirty window display with antiquated ceramic pots and an old poster, promising a sunny vacation in the Mediterranean. The dog is a scraggy mongrel. The walker, wearing a too-large, waxed coat, is also thin, with receding fair hair. The cold has painted his sunken cheeks scarlet. The walker turns the corner, dragging the mongrel behind.

The book reader appears in the café after ten minutes. Getting my journal and pen out, I bend over the page, memorizing the face of a man we came here to kill.

My fancy for the café is easily explained since I am doing my job. I still like to entertain myself with the idea of me sitting here singularly because I have fallen in love with vintage furniture and darkening mirrors. The waiter takes no notice of me, neither does the man with a monster book whom I know to be over sixty and on the run for the past ten years or so.

I sense that the situation is slowly changing, with him starting to acknowledge me. Coming into the café, he hangs his duffle coat on the curved mahogany stand of the kind I would like to have one day in my imaginary flat, together with the worn velvet sofas in the array of jewel colors.

Judging from his clothing, the reader has good taste, but it does not stretch to his choice of paperbacks. He is forever attached to some cheap product. I suspect he picks it up from the used book shops on the main street of this crumbling city, forgotten in the age of the movie posters adorning the peeling walls of the café. The workers, gathering here in the morning, swallow their grub quickly, not paying attention to the elderly beauty of marble tables and the antique gilt of the mirror frames.

The worldly man would choose such a haunt, a man of travels and tales, a man with a mane of curly silver hair, a man of attentive eyes and curt smiles. I cannot allow myself to be misled by them since he is this man and is not to be discounted.

Today, entering the café, his gaze lingered on me, and he smiled a little longer. I looked at him with a calculated measure of interest. I am sure things will progress, but we need to wait. He has been on the loose long enough, killing before, including a woman like me. I have no idea how she looked, but I know what he sees, glancing in my direction.

In the leaden depth of the mirror opposite me, a tall woman drinks her coffee, a woman with a helmet of mad hair the color of pale gold, with a crooked nose and freckled cheeks, a woman of long bony fingers and the seawater eyes. Absent-mindedly wandering around the café, they lit with a genuine surprise. I did not order this cup in front of me.

"From the gentleman in the corner," the waiter's English is heavily accented, impeccably polite. "With compliments to the lady."

This time the book reader's smile is disarmingly charming. He is a handsome man, even at his age. My "Thank you" carries just the required hint of pleasure mixed with embarrassment.

Outside, the scraggy mongrel appears again, sniffing the street garbage bin. Rummaging in my bag, I get a book out. The dog walker also breaks into a satisfied grin, seeing me engrossed in a novel. I am happy that he is happy. For a moment, we smile together, but then he is swept away by the gust of wind. The dog almost flies after him, so thin it is.

"Would you like another cup of coffee?" I say into the stillness of an empty café. "I feel in need of returning a favor."

Now the embarrassment is all his.

The waiter refills his mug as I leave for the brisk walk home

Next time I see the mongrel is in the corner of the bare bathroom. The lush cloud of fragrant bubbles engulfs me so that only my wet hair is visible. I am done and drowned. The skin on my fingertips is wrinkled. My left foot rests on the edge of the tub.

The dog walker sits on the shaky plastic stool, wearing just his boxers and the unbuttoned white shirt. His glasses are all steamed up.

He wipes the tiny drops with the edge of the shirt. Out of all his small movements, this is the one I like the best. It gets under my skin, traveling my veins, making me liquid. I am already almost submerged under the water, so I sigh audibly. The mongrel timidly tries to growl, the walker smiles.

"Just wait, old man," he promises. "We will go outside soon." The dog contentedly lies down, close enough to the wobbly stool leg.

The walker is very good with dogs and children. He is also an excellent shot which will come in handy tomorrow. We all have names, but we never mention them out loud for the sake of security. Not the fake ones from the current passports, soon to be destroyed, nor the real ones, which I sometimes have trouble remembering.

Although The Twins, sitting in the car next to the reader's flat, have already reported that he is firmly at home, we cannot risk the walker accompanying me to my cheap hotel. The bath in his place will have to suffice.

The Twins cannot be more unlike each other, but we have been calling them so for the past ten years, and they seem not to mind. They are the techies, providing the surveillance and the final deep clean. The Twins come in after the walker, who will wait tomorrow afternoon outside the reader's house.

The glasses back on his also crooked nose, he looks at me hesitantly.

"Is it a firm arrangement?"

I roll my eyes, he smiles.

"I remember this expression from the first time I saw you on stage," he strokes my foot, taking it between his warm hands. "I thought you were a great actor."

I tickle his fingers with my toe.

"You know I am no good."

That is our private joke, and he is yet to miss the beat. He never does. In the army, he served in a sharpshooting unit. He could have killed the reader on the street, but this godforsaken hole of the city is so tiny that anyone on the roof will inevitably attract attention.

"I know you are the trouble."

He kisses the round protruding bone on my ankle. The mongrel sighs heavily.

"We will take you home," promises the walker. "This is the last assignment, buddy. We will fly back and live in the white house next to the sea. The beach will be all yours, and we will get the boat."

I have heard this so many times before, but somehow today, I want to believe him.

"Absolutely," I assure the walker. "He is picking me up from the café at two in the afternoon."

The reader teaches English in the local community college. Now I understand why he only comes to the café thrice a week.

The walker winks at me.

"Did he promise to show you his stamp collection?"

I dive in the clouds of foam, emerging with a bubbly head.

"Almost. Local archeological finds. The reader used to be a real professor, and the old habits die hard."

The walker nods.

"Tomorrow, they shall die for real."

We both laugh, and the mongrel growls again, this time tenderly.

That night, I dream of the dog on the beach, hearing its excited barking. A baby splashes in the hissing surf. I cannot discern whether it is a boy or a girl but decide it to be irrelevant. I am more concerned about the boat drifting into the milky fog. Making out the walker's shadow, I hear his shout, but the words sink into the sea, lost in the space between us.

I think about this dream on the way to the reader's flat, traversing the mantle of frosty fog, which has descended on the narrow alleys.

My host is courteous in an old-fashioned manner, and we speak of things insignificant. The fog is so thick I can barely see the reader.

The walker is invisible to me, but I know he is there. I also would like to know who played in the surf, although I do not believe in dreams.

The reader makes quite a good coffee. His hands are trembling slightly, and his breathing becomes heavier. I already decided where to place him. A sunken easy chair faces the door through which the walker should enter in about seven minutes. The performance is carefully orchestrated, reminiscent of my theater days. When we settle in the white house on the seashore, I might try teaching drama in the high school. Dreaming of it, I feel the hungry hand on my shoulder. The sooner we begin, the quicker everything will be over.

I am in danger of being soaked in blood, but I am supple, always avoiding the cascade of ruby splatters. The reader turns out to be a good kisser. After a couple of minutes, I put him in the chair. My breath is also calculatedly faster. The zipper goes down, and he wiggles free.

Hearing the creak of the floor outside, I engage my mouth in work. Before the shots deafen me momentarily, I notice warts in the groin of an almost dead man. They remind me somehow, disgustingly, of mushrooms.

3 Ailments – Benjamin Eric (he/him)

I'm incredibly ill. I think. Apparently, you can inherit family trauma. If that is true, what else can we inherit? Is that what preexisting conditions are? That might just be an insurance thing, but I'm not sure.

I need a doctor. I feel like hell, and I know my mind is breaking down. There is something wrong. There's a list in my pocket of my three ailments that I hope the doctor can help me with. He has a white mustache and a Tufts medical degree framed on the wall. So far, he seems nice enough.

Good thing I memorized the list because the paper is in my pants' pocket, and I had to take them off for the initial exam. He asks me what seems to be the problem today. I tell him there are three concerns I have, and he makes the helpful suggestion of starting with the first one.

"I might be an alcoholic," I say. Not much of a proclamation. It does not feel liberating or healing.

His next question seems reasonable. How many drinks do I have a night? I tell him I am not sure, but I have at least one glass of wine or a beer with dinner. His next question is silly. He asks if I've tried to quit, and I tell him why would I quit if I am not sure I'm an alcoholic or not. Maybe he needs more context, so I explain that my brother and grandfather were both alcoholics. My grandfather drank so much that he died during a drunken stupor when he fell down a flight of stairs and cracked open the back of his head.

He suggests I see a therapist or a social worker to delve deeper. I request he draw blood or run x-rays to determine if I am addicted to alcohol and to what extent.

For some reason that is not possible. How can there be no tests that can tell if and how much someone may be addicted to something? They have tests to see if someone has diabetes or cancer. They can even tell you what type of diabetes you have or how much cancer is in your body.

Apparently, the medical technology does not exist. The doctor's only advice, other than talking to a mental health professional, is to try and cut back on drinking and see how that goes.

We move on and go into the second ailment.

"I forgot how to speak Spanish."

The doctor is acting like he does not understand so I repeat myself. To clarify, he asks if I ever knew Spanish and I tell him only a few words and phrases, but my grandmother did. She spoke Spanish her whole life. If trauma can be inherited, why not language? All history lives in the brain.

Grandma used to speak Spanish to my mother and even me. She was born in Buffalo and lived in Brooklyn for many years but grew up in Spanish speaking households. Her parents were from Ronda, Spain and spoke with that famous lisp. I demonstrate the lisp to the doctor with one of the few phrases I know, but that doesn't seem to help his confusion.

I go on and tell him that she had nicknames for me in Spanish. She used to call me, "mi chico de ojos azules." I get emotional sharing that memory with the physician and he does not seem to understand that I need his diagnosis. So I ask him again:

"Why can't I speak Spanish?"

He seems frazzled. Maybe I went to the wrong doctor. He tells me if I never actually learned to speak the language, then I never forgot. It's odd that I have to explain to him the recent study about how we can inherit our family's trauma. He begins to lecture me, but my confidence is fading.

This was my mistake. I should have gone to a neurologist. I ask for a recommendation, but he says any neurologist will tell me the same thing. I'm getting ready to leave and he asks, what is the last issue I am having. Even though I have lost faith, I share with him.

"I can't get an erection."

He asks how long this has been going on for. I tell him for about thirteen hours, but I think he hears me say "days" instead. I describe my girlfriend to him and how wonderful our relationship has been lately. We've been having sex all the time and she drives me wild.

I tell the doctor about how excited she makes me. That she'll often sit naked on the edge of the bed with her legs spread and her toes pressed down against the floor on the balls of her feet to steady herself. She'll then take her finger and graze the tip from the bottom of her pussy all the way up to her clit and stroke it gently clockwise. She has me massage her breasts as she breathes into my ear and her breath tickles my entire body and makes my bones shiver. She does this until I can't contain myself and drop to my knees and begin licking where she was massaging. Her moans make me so hard and when she grabs my hair, I lose all control, and I love the way she tastes so much that sometimes I'll just cum right there before her.

The cum sticks to my thigh hair and I try to catch my breath while I keep licking her at the same time until she cums too and my mouth and chin are drenched with her.

The doctor seems interested in the story, but I can't tell if he is taking notes or not. I hope he is following this because I need his help. I know for a fact that my parents stopped having sex the last twenty or so years of their life and I would kill myself if I inherited whatever condition inflicted that upon them.

Surprisingly, the doctor begins scribbling on a pad and hands me a prescription. He says this should help with erectile dysfunction.

"That's it?" I ask.

He just nods and recommends I see a therapist for the other issues I disclosed to him today. He also suggests I try not drinking to see if that helps with my erections. I think I'll try the medication first.

Picking up the pills at the pharmacy is easy enough. Although, the pills aren't covered by insurance, so swiping my credit card hurts. At least pharmacists don't ask intruding questions. You just pay and be on your way. I remember trying to get cough medicine in Austria. I wasn't sick, but I needed it for my jet lag to get to sleep. The pharmacist kept asking me questions regarding my symptoms and it's not like I could tell them it was for recreation.

I know he was just trying to help, but I didn't want to explain everything. This doctor, here in the States, wasn't so great but hopefully he'll help me get a boner again. And maybe this medicine will help me remember Spanish the next time I cum.

Fingers crossed.

NON-FICTION

The Waters I Swim In – Beth Anne Macdonald (she/her)

I make my way to the edge of the riverbank. Moving through familiar territory, signs I've been here before, left like bookmarks or crumbs of cookies, mark my path. Caution makes my steps slow. Intention makes them steady. I come to the bank of this river quite often. Sometimes I am content to sit, eyes unfocused, only half paying attention to the water flowing past me. Other times, I am alert for a place low enough so I might walk right in. Heraclitus believed you could never step in the same river twice. He understood life to be in a constant state of change. Eternal flux. I believe this too. It seems as soon as I become *sure* of some truth: a fact about a thing, a person, a situation, it changes. Or I change. Time and perspective reveal something hidden. The whole shifting and transforming anew.

In the Book of John, Jesus tells a Samaritan woman, "But whosoever drinketh of the water that I shall give him shall never thirst; but the water that I shall give him shall be in him a well of water springing up into everlasting life." Science tells us water makes up over half the weight of a human body. About 60% on average. Water covers about 70% of the earth's surface. Perhaps if we believe in evolution, we have a vague sense of life long past, created in the very first ocean. Maybe we even sense the connection between those ancient waters and the waters of our mother's womb. Only after leaving the primordial and amniotic seas do we take on our earthly weight.

Whatever our convictions, story, or science, water is necessary for life. There is no question of errancy here. I know through my blood, made partially of water, flows my life. Water. Blood. Life. *Life Blood.* A dictionary tells us lifeblood is something essential, *a vital or life-giving force.* I believe this too. My lifeblood carries all that is essential to me: DNA, experiences, memories. Stories. What came before and what is yet to be. Versions of the truth of who I am. My lifeblood is my nature and my nurture. I think about these things as I sit on the riverbank and consider my family.

I think about the waters of my youth. Water as falling snow, forming icicles off the slanted roof. Freezing solid, supporting fishing shanties, and snowmobiles. Friday night fish fry. Piles of snow, creating cotton candy shadows in the dawn of a new day. A day only slightly warmer than the day before and only if you are paying attention. Snow finally melting into slush, seeping into streams, swollen with abundance. Streams flowing into a pond, a lake, an ocean. A container circular in its essence. Oval. Ovum. Egg. These are also the things I think about while sitting on the riverbank. Memories piling up like weathered bits of debris after a storm. Until finally, I think about the Lake and the day my family pulled up anchor, sailing into uncharted waters.

When I step into the stream, letting the current wash over me as I submerge into its slippery depths, it is not to be freed of my sins so that I might enter the Kingdom of God, as in Acts 22:16, "And now why tarriest thou? Arise, and be baptized, and wash away thy sins, calling on the name of the Lord." For I do not believe I am unworthy by the mere fact of my birth. Nor do I believe I am further marred by the second fact of being born a female. No, as a descendent of Eve and most recently the daughter of Elizabeth, I hold my head high. I am clear-eyed as I step into this river, a digital flow of information, searching for the headwaters of my family history so that I might claim the stories of my inheritance.

I dive down into the channels of my mind where my muse is waiting. "What did you see in your dream last night?" she asks.

"I dreamt about my family tree," I say. "I saw my hand running over its branches, green and gold against the page, and drops of blood were falling from my fingertips."

This fucking tree. A constant, irritating reminder, it is the men in my family who insist on telling everyone's story. A tree, rising from its trunk, always thrusting upwards, demanding a place in the sun. Sap as seminal fluid. Lineage shown in straight lines. Neat little boxes scattered evidence of spilled seed. The entire image of a family tree, an homage to the penis. Of course it is. Trace the word homage back to its Latin phallic root of homo and, well man, you get it. Not surprising that *his-story* is so self-involved, really. Care to disagree? Take a supple switch, punish the disobedient. Do not spare the rod either. Sixty-six books of the Bible, every single one written by a man. Mansplaining my inheritance. Mansplaining everyone's inheritance. Do I sound *hysterical*? Blame it on my womb.

So, I've given up on my family tree. I'm tired of scraped knees and constantly picking splinters out of my palms as I move away from branches that crack under the weight of my scrutiny. I'm exhausted by the efforts to climb. Tree top. Mountain top. Penthouse suite. Heaving and hauling myself upward in an endless pursuit of... what? Believing at the crown, in that pinnacle place, the truth will finally be revealed?

"What can ever be truly known, my child?" my muse asks of me.

She tosses me an apple. A rosy reminder of the inside joke I have lately forgotten. "Did you really forget?" she chides.

My Stories Are Not Forbidden Fruit.

My Family Is Not A Tree.

I am not a limb, a branch, part of and yet forever separate. Something to be hacked off in a fit of rage. I am not fuel by way of example. Chopped up to feed the fire under those who dare to ask the questions.

"Go down," my muse says. "Dig deep into the soil of your remembrance. There you will find water and, in the water, in the generations of your blood, you will find life." My Family Is Water.

I am a part of a great sea. Our collective history flows through me. I am one drop in an ocean of stories across the ages. Each beat of my heart moves my blood, a pulsing ebb and flow found in the tides of our life-giving waters.

But I am careful. I know how dangerous water can be. How dangerous memory can be. It doesn't take much water to drown a person, and the truth, well, the truth, can be a fickle bitch. Like a riptide or a fast current, she can pull you under before you even know what's happening. I take things slow. Sometimes it's better to stop swimming and float for a while. Catch my breath.

Renata says, "You know your father told your mother God gave her cancer because she was disobedient. That it was her own fault she was sick." I stop breathing. Floating there in the sunny hustle and bustle of Panera Bread where we are having breakfast, I'm unable to swim any further.

Some days I tread water. It's the best I can do. I climb the attic steps and pull the string to the single bulb hanging from the rafter. Pick one box over another for no apparent reason. Grade school photos of me. My brother's baby book. My mother's medical records. Brittle relics of the living and the dead.

I am wary too about where I stop to drink. Staying away from water that looks brackish. By its very appearance, I know it is not life-giving. Some water, though, even with movement, carries disease invisible to the eye but poisonous to the spirit. These are dangerous waters indeed. As I wade through the years, I remember the first time my father told me I was going to burn in Hell. I was thirteen. I will not linger here to fill my cup.

Dipping my feet into the sandy shallows, facts, like minnows, dart, then retreat. What year did my grandmother graduate from Normal School? Answer, 1929. When did my parents buy their first house? Answer, 1965. The same year they were married. When was the release of the movie 'Annie'? Answer, 1982. The summer I visited my grandparents and went to the dentist for the first time.

Periodically, I cast out a line out to see what I might catch. Like anyone hoping to reel in a prize, I craft my bait with care. I try different lures: emails, cards in the mail, occasionally a phone call if I can track down a number. People, I've discovered, like stubborn fish, will resist even repeated attempts to get tangled up in old family storylines. Even if, or maybe especially if, they were once old friends. I wish I could convince them I mean no harm. I just want to talk for a bit and then I will let them go. *I know this note is unexpected,* I write. *I've thought of you often since mom passed away*, I say into the phone. No response.

But oh, sometimes, a tug is felt. The pole bends! "Hello Beth, my mind is whirling with memories about your mom," a close friend of my mother's responds to a Facebook message. "Dearest Beth Anne, how happy I am to hear from you. What an amazing gift to receive your letter," a high school teacher writes to me. Then there was the day I caught the big one. The one that didn't get away. "In a nutshell–yes your dad is my nut case brother." The response to an email, subject title: Potential Relative (Niece)! A break in the levee. What was unknown is now known in a flash flood of detail. I drink them all in.

Our inherited stories are streams and creeks winding away over time and distance, only to return, once again becoming part of our whole. What memories live in our family waters? Are carried in our blood? Embodied patterns that move beneath the surface. Known and unknown.

Known: My mother loved to rock in a rocking chair, like my grandmother, like her mother before her. This motion, this habit, lives in my body now too. This is what I do. I rock back and forth. It is the motion of the tide. The motion of blood and breath. Dipping slowly in and out, oars move through water. Bringing me back to shore.

No longer unknown: great-uncles, different family tributaries, far apart, come together in me. Men who moved to New Jersey decades ago. One stayed. One did not. No one ever told me when I came here thirty years ago, I followed a streambed. Dried up, abandoned, but somehow still known.

Known: My brother is twelve years younger than I am.

No longer unknown: My uncle is twelve years younger than my father.

Patterns emerge. Time and perspective revealing what is hidden. Life in a constant state of change. Eternal flux.

Perhaps we are closer in temperament to forms of ancient fish that came before us. Called back to the waters of our origins. Is this genealogy? Traveling thousands of digital miles through ancestral waters and earthly pathways to search for the stories of our belonging. To know and be known.

Yet, I am mindful of how long I gaze into these still pools. Myths warn me not to become obsessed with the reflections of the past, lest I forget to live in the present. Or to listen only to the echoes of what came before, instead of using my voice to change what can yet be.

At long last, I arrive at the Lake, the place where my family became unmoored. Water always seeks to find its gravitational equilibrium. It is here I hope to find mine.

Lighting-Up–a Family Tradition – Iris Leona Marie Cross (she/her)

Great-aunt Sugar plonks her overweight self in the front passenger seat reserved for her.

"Somebody, come hold this jug, quick. The water's spilling!"

And it spills on Sugar's frilly, floral, cotton frock. Skipping down the front steps, I rush to help since the others are already waiting in the sweltering car, engine running. Selina, my mother, a stickler for time, is at the steering wheel "steupsing." Great-aunt Gigi is in the backseat fanning herself and my older sister with a Christian Endeavor Hymnal.

"Did you all remember to bring matches?" Sugar asks in her usual bossy manner.

"Yes," replies great-aunt Gigi. "Hurry and close the door! Selina's already vexed."

Uncle Arthur, Sugar's long-suffering, henpecked husband, is in his wood and wicker rocking chair looking on from the porch, eager for us to depart. With his wife gone, he gets a much-desired breather from her commands in octaves typically rising to a crescendo: "Arthuur, Arthuuur, Arthuuuur, come here!" He can now enjoy a puff of Marlborough and a tipple of Teacher's whiskey without harassment.

****

So began our outings to Lapeyrouse, the crème de la crème of Trinidad's cemeteries, when I was a child. With expertly sculpted idols adorning many tombs and ornate, monstrous mausoleums housing the bones of the once rich and famous Europeans, Lapeyrouse was a spooky place in a child's eyes. It still is. Its carved-out rows, blocks, and paved, numbered, signposted streets running east, west, north, and south is reminiscent of a living city. The only difference is its residents are dead.

Each year on November 1, All Saints' Day, my family visited Lapeyrouse to pay tribute to my great-grandmother, Mama, who died before I was born. My sister, great-aunts, and I packed into my mother's second-hand, moss green American Rambler motor car, which she drove with enviable expertise. We loaded the car with paint, paintbrushes, rags, vases, candles, matches, an array of flowers, and a cocoyea broom—paraphernalia to ensure Mama's burial plot was immaculate. Great-aunt Sugar always insisted on holding the large, white enamel jug brimful of water, a must-have, in case the cemetery taps were dry.

Lapeyrouse was abuzz with activity as families paid their respects to the deceased. Hustlers at the towering iron front gates, hungry for a few dollars, hounded everyone entering the cemetery for a quick clean-and-paint job. Alongside the drive were vendors, chanting, "Get your fresh flowers!"—often stolen from already-beautified graves.

Lighting-Up, Festival of the Dead, wasn't a morbid experience. I found it entertaining, educational, and enlightening because of my great-aunts. Their vivid storytelling traced Mama's journey from her parents' (ex-slaves) sugarcane estate in St Lucia to Trinidad. Here she met and married Papa, an immigrant himself but from Barbados.

Mama appeared to be a formidable, entrepreneurial, philanthropic, religious, no-nonsense woman who kicked unfaithful Papa out of the family home. Papa returned home one evening from his supervisory job at the abattoir to find his belongings strewn on the street. Undaunted by the collapse of her marriage, Mama bought an estate of cocoa, coffee, and citrus, purchased houses to let, and established one of the first car rental services in Trinidad.

My great-aunts' efforts to correct each other or provide the missing information in Mama's saga intrigued me every time. Lighting-Up was one of those rare occasions harmony reigned between the two warring sisters. Their verbal warfare and tug-of-war over pots and pans were a regular occurrence in our house. In these heated sessions, Gigi and Sugar argued, at maximum volume, over who was the rightful owner of the cooking utensils in question. It's a surprise there were no physical injuries, though they both suffered the blow of hurtful words slung back and forth.

"This is MY house! You can't tell me what I can and can't use," Sugar yelled.

"We should never have signed over the house to you. Mama left this house for all her children. You tricked us."

"I paid you and the others fair and square. Even offered to let you continue living here rent-free."

"And in return, you persecute me. But one day, I'll have my own house."

"The only house you'll have is your grave."

Gigi usually snapped. Filling a glass with water and praying over it, she'd sprinkle the Holy Water throughout the length and breadth of the house. For every step Gigi took, she denounced the devil, Sugar, her younger sister.

 "Get thee behind me, Satan!"

Yet at Lighting-Up, the two sisters united to regale us with stories about Mama, as dust from the swishing strokes of the cocoyea broom and pungent fumes from the wet paint invaded our lungs. Goaded by the incorrigible duo, I dumped weeds, unruly vines, pebbles, and dirt on top of the adjacent allotment. Etched in black on a white headstone was the name, Blanche Fraser.

Lighting-Up was the only time I obeyed Gigi and Sugar, no questions asked. Who was Blanche Fraser, and why did they insist on defiling her grave annually with my help? In my teens, I discovered Blanche's identity. "That jezebel was our father's mistress," Sugar said. "We have no respect for her, living or dead." Blanche Fraser was the temptress who had beguiled Papa.

Each year I learned something new about Mama while we swept dust, scrubbed moss, and scraped flaking paint from the wire-fenced, concrete-paved allotment. When it was spanking clean and decorated with gerberas, ixoras, roses, and tiger lilies from our garden, we took turns to light candles.

****

As Sugar had proclaimed, the only house Gigi got was her grave. A few years later, Sugar joined Gigi, side by side, at Lapeyrouse. It wasn't the same without them. My mother and I continued the tradition tinged with sadness.

"I wonder who'll do this when I'm gone," she mused as we swept, scrubbed, painted, and decorated the enclosure with flowers before lighting candles.

We took care not to dump rubbish or step on Blanche's grave since we harboured no ill will toward her. Unlike Gigi and Sugar, we hadn't experienced the family turmoil Blanche had created. My mother was born long after Papa's infidelity and eviction. By the time I came along, Mama and Papa were already dead.

"I wonder who'll do this when I'm gone," my mother repeated. I remained silent. A guilty knot swelled up in my tummy. Unbeknownst to her, I intended to leave Trinidad for good, as my sister did when she turned eighteen.

Decades later, life has come full circle. I have returned to the family home in Trinidad. Every year, on November 1, I clean and beautify the allotment that now houses a new resident—my mother. As I gaze teary-eyed at the flickering candles, I, like my mother, wonder who'll do this when I'm gone.

Climbing the Walls – Anita Howard (she/her)

Sunlight is the most enduring memory of my first trip to London. It was glorious and intense on the battlement walk at the Tower of London, as my father held me up to look over the River Thames. I was four years old, aware of very little beyond the unusually hot weather.

In later years I would enjoy the story of the hasty exit we had just made from the armoury in the White Tower, where my older cousin had drawn the gaze of everyone within earshot by looking up at Henry VIII's generously-proportioned battle armour and remarking in carrying tones, "Wow! He sure had big ….!"

As we laughed together, the lives of other families were being torn apart in the country we had left only days earlier. The Queen of England's cousin, Lord Louis Mountbatten, regularly spent the summer at Mullaghmore Bay in Co. Sligo. That morning, in the same blazing sunshine, he had taken his family out on a fishing trip. When they were well out to sea, the IRA bomb concealed on their boat the night before was detonated.

The explosion killed Mountbatten, his daughter's elderly mother-in-law, and two children. This assassination, and the later Warrenpoint ambush, made the day—August 27, 1979—the deadliest of the Troubles up to then. The news had begun to filter through on the car radio as we drove down from our home in Liverpool to visit my uncle and aunt in Surrey. It was being discussed all around us with disbelief and growing anger as we made our way through the Tower of London, which is not only a tourist attraction, but a working British military base.

Our hurried exit from the White Tower was not really prompted by my cousin's outspokenness but my parents' fear that their Irish accents would be detected by those around them. It was their first experience of that fear in two decades of English life.

In the years that followed, I would come to understand that fear myself. Most second-generation Irish children do not retain their parents' accent, but I was to be one of the exceptions. This was largely ignored during my years at primary school, but in secondary school it was noticed at last.

Year after bloody year the Troubles had continued, and my classmates and I were increasingly aware that there was a political edge to being Irish in Britain. On British television, those suspected of connections with Republican terrorism had their voices dubbed by actors when they were interviewed as a feature of Margaret Thatcher's policy of ensuring they were outlawed.

Perhaps this, among other things, sent its own message about the power and implication of an Irish voice, especially when it was heard in the wrong place—and an English school, at that time, could count as the wrong place under certain unsupervised conditions.

There might have been a hint of affection in the playground chant of "Anita is an IRA spy," mainly because it was applied to such an unlikely subject; I was probably the least rebellious child in the school, and subversion did not come naturally to me. But not every child was able to stop at teasing.

Insults like, "Hello, Anita, you wee Irish whore" and "wee bitch" would be thrown at me, the "wee" coming directly from the manner of speech associated with Northern Ireland, where the aggressors were sure my terrorist connections must lie. On several occasions the bullying turned physical, with threats of much worse, simply because of the way I spoke.

The assailants were usually that singular type of boy who seems moved to work out his own concept of national pride on the quietest girl within range of his fists. I had never expressed any sympathy for the IRA, but that was beside the point. It was enough for my classmates that I sounded Irish and was making no obvious attempt to sound very much like them. If I wasn't one of them, I must, of necessity, be one of *them*. The idea that I might simply be my own person seemed to be more threatening than anything else.

Every interaction carries a lesson, but we interpret those lessons for ourselves. These encounters did not teach me that it would be a good idea to change my accent. Instead they left me certain that I would never fit into the world around me and even open to the idea that it would be best not to try.

Inevitably the young patriots of the schoolyard went too far, and their activities could no longer be hidden. My mother intervened; the worst offenders were warned off by the school authorities with a severity that was never forgotten. In return I was further isolated, and got through each day by speaking as little as possible outside my own mind, where, of course, conditions were always perfect, and defences could never be breached because I'd forged every last one of them.

Years later, a blazing summer again darkens around us. I've long since left England to make my home in Cork, but I have become a regular visitor to the Tower when I return to London. I know every inch of the place that is open to visitors: the towers, the flightless ravens, the ghosts, the long list of close prisoners. And, of course, Henry VIII's battle armour. Like all the patriots in my life, there is no doubt that he certainly had big...ideas.

Haven't we all? For these days I can see even more clearly that those ancient walls of blood, despair, and betrayal are only a pale reflection of the rarefied walls we each create in our mind. Walls built, like their physical counterparts, not to charm small children, but to safeguard our beliefs about who we are or want to be.

And then I think of others, who managed to live their lives beyond the schoolyard and its fortresses. My uncle, a proud Englishman, who was stunned by the Mountbatten assassination but welcomed us with open arms on that sunlit day and, without a word about events on the news, set about making our trip to London the wonderful experience that it was. The principal of my secondary school, who noticed me standing alone day after day, quietly asked other children why it was that they were allowing that to happen and sent them up to me, whatever their protestations, to ask if I was all right. And, near to the end of my time in the school, the tough-looking girl who swept up to me and told me with absolute sincerity that she loved to hear me speak because I sounded exactly like her Nan.

Ancestral walls. We move with them or against them. Moving beyond them is another question, and, when a clear blue sky can so swiftly give way to trauma, bloodshed, and division, perhaps the reality is that there are walls we can never escape. But maybe it's only now that I am beginning to learn what was there for me on the battlements on that day in 1979. When we find our walls around us, we can let them close us into our own darkness, or else allow them to carry us up towards the clear light of day and whatever on earth that light has to teach us.

Fifteen Minutes – Jill P. Strachan (she/her)

Close enough to touch,
my story disclosed actions
of man next to me.

The three of us spent fifteen arduous, humorless minutes together in April 1975. The fifteen minutes felt interminable. They were. The department chair's small office had windows looking south to the courtyard. We were on the third floor. It was late morning as sunlight (an extraordinary occurrence in perpetually clouded central New York state) streamed in. Chair RC sat behind his desk, perpendicular to the window, with a bookcase behind him. Tenured Professor DBR, formerly my potential PhD advisor, sat by the window, and I, graduate student, and complainant, by the door, which was shut. DBR's and my chair were close together. Without vigilance, our arms could have spilled off our arm rests to touch the other. I held on to my right arm with my left hand to prevent any unexpected, nauseating physical contact. In preparation, I had dispensed several pep talks to myself: speak without hesitation and tears, keep sentences direct and short, and breathe no matter what. I could not eat my breakfast; just as well, because I would have thrown up.

Worrying about the impending meeting, it had not occurred to me how unsettling it would be to inhabit the same space as Professor DBR, although I had agreed to the meeting after reporting his behavior to RC. I was shaky, emotional, and trying to control my demeanor—it was nerve-wracking to be so close to him. My voice might have wavered a bit, but my anger fortified and prevented me from crying. I started with my organized litany of oddities and grievances, enumerating uncomfortable encounters, from the first one, DBR standing at the bus stop across from the building where I lived. The next day he asked me, *Tell me which room is yours?* There were other unasked-for-personal remarks. *I dreamed about you on Sunday night. Why do you try so hard to be unattractive without succeeding?* Finally, the phone call from the week before. He had to tell me at 1:15 AM he loved me.

DBR denied everything. At one point, he thundered, *I don't know what she's talking about. I've been impotent for 20 years.* He blamed medication for his conduct. These statements were the closest he would ever come to admitting his behavior, much less delivering an apology for his shattering ignorance.

RC sat in his chair. He agreed to my requested academic separation from DBR.

Our encounter ended. I walked into the hallway. I was relieved yet felt no satisfaction.

Afterwards, I wrote in my journal: *Show me the man who understands/no, just concedes the existence of the continued <u>sexual</u> assault against women by men. Time heals and my memories of this will also fade, but some part of me will remember enough to make me wonder every time there is a remote chance, every time there is ambiguity, oh yes. Thank you, Dr. Robertson.* (April 22, 1975)

There were no organizational repercussions for Dr. Robertson. The academic system fully protected him. His tenure was not in question. His career continued unabated and untrammeled. The system cleared him to harass other women.

But these fifteen minutes were a life course correction for me. I did not appreciate their overwhelming impact until several decades later, when I could look back at choices I had made. With another adviser, I finished my PhD from afar in 1981. Then I quit the academic life that I loved and for which I had trained for a decade. I was still young but deeply disillusioned.

> Water drips on stone—
> sexual harassment's toll
> erodes over time.

Billboards in Mesquite, TX – Kristin H. Sample (she/her)

Driving on 635 you can see North Texas through gaps in the billboards.

Got Jesus?

...and other churchy quips that speak more of religiosity and marketing than spirituality. Not far from any church here, is a place like Dreamerz. Spelled with a "z" for extra pizzazz. Their billboard is tucked in between one with a verse from Ephesians and one that reads "Women Regret Abortions."

Do they?

And you know what happens at Dreamerz in the dark hours. Flesh and sin and an honest dollar made and spent. Go. Watch those strong thighs slide down an oiled pole. If you have more paper for devotion, go in the private room where cheap champagne washes down hot wings. A bouncer the girls call Uncle will let you know if you get too close.

On Saturday night, you can bury your face in breasts and then on Sunday morning, you can bury your face in your hands.

But what of Friday? Are there billboards for Friday?

Yes, a new one just went up. Paid for by the proud booster club. *Pony Up, Mesquite*, it reads. Two black boys in full color adorn the billboard. Blue jerseys and shoulder pads that look grotesque in any other context but a football field. They are the two men whose lithe bodies will carry the town to glory on Friday night. Or to ruin. The whole town watching. Hot fluorescent lights illuminating pristine turf under the immense, black Texas sky.

New rules say these boys can be paid for their likeness. Make the most of their small-town gladiator careers. Buy a Nissan for their mamas. Maybe buy it at the dealership owned by the fat, red-faced booster president. He drives by the new billboard in his Suburban every day. A cross dangles from his rearview mirror.

Where the boys live there is a basketball hoop without a net. Weeds poke through cracks in the parking lot pavement.

Legacy – Dixie Kootz-Eades (she/her)

I am Maxine's legacy, her mirror, and as I share our stories, I beget others like me. Together, we create a community large enough to be seen, and not to be forgotten. Time is restructured when we are brought together, creating a through-line of illness and abuse that crosses all generations, ethnicities, and cultures. We are a people that are ignored, spoken over, villainized, and often forgotten. This changes now. I will not forget Maxine; she didn't make it, but I will. Each of us that survives abuse and mental illness and then goes on to thrive, become the legacy of those before us who haven't been so lucky.

I was only two years old when Maxine died from ovarian cancer. I can just barely remember when my dad left for Alaska to be with her in her final days. He was responsible for claiming her body and taking care of her estate. This wasn't hard, hell, she didn't even have an apartment to sort through. My aunts ended up with most of her possessions: a box of jewelry and a small envelope left for me. She had been living off the grid, homeless, having moved up to Alaska so that the government couldn't spy on her. She didn't see a doctor until it was too late for the same reason. The way I see it, it was her mental illness, and not the cancer, that really killed her.

What I know of Maxine's story begins back when she was in high-school. This was when she confided in her mother that she was being abused by her brothers. Her mother accused her of lying, and soon, the entire family was calling her, 'crazy Maxine.' Her father, and biggest supporter, had passed on a few years before and was unable to protect her. Isolated and enduring ongoing abuse, Maxine did what any young woman would do: she got out of the house. She tied the knot of unstable matrimony at the age of sixteen and proceeded to give birth to four children. Unfortunately, her marriage unraveled during her twenties, in part, because she had begun to exhibit symptoms of schizophrenia. Her mental illness now also became the fuel her family used to gaslight her, adding to the trauma that most likely triggered her illness in the first place. In our family, Maxine's 'craziness' spread to

351

anyone that believed her; giving them the honorific 'Crazy' as well. Maxine's younger brother received it, but my dad managed to avoid getting this honorific, calling Maxine crazy in public but privately affirming the abuse. The cognitive dissonance I had from these opposing viewpoints laid foundation for how I interacted with people. I grew up loving Maxine, while simultaneously trying to ensure that I never became like her. Consequently, because she had passed, I spent much more time with her emotional abusers, though, to my father's credit, he refused to spend any time with her sexual abusers. We spent a lot of time with Maxine's mother and her ex-husband, and I learned that these were the normal people of the world. I grew up expecting people to distrust the mentally ill. I subconsciously learned that victims were always at fault. I learned that if anyone was not financially, physically, and mentally well, they were lazy and therefore lesser people. This was the framework for goodness that I applied to myself, believing that being called 'crazy' was the worst thing that could happen to me.

Maxine became both a memory and a ghost to me. Since Dad only talked about her abuse or schizophrenia, I latched onto every positive memory I had of her, real and imagined. Before she died, Maxine gave me a miniature tea-set, hand-painted with forget-me-not flowers. Unable to remember anything about her but her fluffy brown hair and the way she sauteed morels, this tea-set became my most treasured possession. It connected me to my forgotten grandma—the grandma nobody talked about.

Grandma Maxine became increasingly important to me as our stories began to intertwine. When I was molested at eight years old, I received a second gift from her: she became my guardian angel, and an angel of comfort for the sexually abused. Maxine became the one person in my family that I could talk to, that I knew would believe me. Even at eight, I knew her story, and not to say anything to anyone else. I imagined my grandma looking down on me and sharing my pain. I imagined her listening to me when my friends ignored me. She became the rock I clung to through the decade-long depression that washed over me.

The day I graduated from eighth grade, I received a third gift from Maxine. For my eighth grade graduation, she had asked my aunt to give me a small box and envelope. The note inside it read, "I'm proud of you for making it this far. Love, Grandma Maxine." In the box was her Mother's Day ring, set with the birthstones of her children. It warmed my heart to know that when I was still an infant, she had written the note and asked my aunts to hold the ring for me until I finished eighth grade. Although separated by different lifetimes, my grandma had not forgotten me.

While Maxine's ring became a source of comfort throughout my life, it could not treat my depression and PTSD. My first flashback occurred when I was a freshman in high school, and I began to dwell on my trauma. Of course, I couldn't show this; my dad believed that depression was a sign of sin. I was not allowed to be sad for any moderate length of time; even deaths were only mourned until the funeral ended. Alone, I internalized that being molested was my fault and that God would hate me until I fixed myself. Part of this new devotion to God involved forgiving all people that harmed me. Having never learned boundaries, this forgiveness was at the cost of recognizing any assaults I endured. Over time, the more pain I forgave someone for, the stronger I loved them. I was assaulted six more times between the ages of fifteen and twenty, four times by a man that suggested leaving his girlfriend for me. I began to take an unpleasant comfort in what I had discovered long before, that I was to carry on the trauma that had begun with Maxine.

Fortunately, at my Christian college, I met a so-called 'bad boy,' and in a moment of desperation for love, I stumbled into a healthy relationship. My now spouse, is a feminist who listens to me, respects my ideas, and most importantly, got my consent to even kiss me. A few years of this relationship gave me the emotional space to realize that the 'love' I had felt for my abusers, was actually trauma-bonding and dependence. Once I had correctly named these feelings, I began to learn how to heal. I finally really learned how to live for, and by, myself. Thanks to my spouse, years of therapy, and plenty of luck, I have learned to surround myself with good people that help facilitate my healing, and I have learned self-love. In many ways, I am now the healthiest mentally, that I have ever been.

Healing, however, cannot cure all the effects of trauma. With my emotional maturity I have received a fourth gift from Maxine. As the true mirror of her life that I have become, at twenty-seven, I have been diagnosed with schizophrenia. True to character, my dad believes that my mental wellness is dependent entirely on my physical wellness. These past few years, watching my childhood worries about being "crazy," become my reality, has in many ways not been as bad as I imagined; in other ways, it's been much worse. Very rarely do I feel 'crazy,' and even rarer do people perceive me with such stigma, yet, I have watched my world fall apart. Despite being near the top of my class in both high-school and college, in grad-school my mental illnesses began to take charge. While my symptoms have been developing, I have watched a part of myself leave. I have lost the parts of me that were able to handle complex conversations and extensive responsibilities. No longer am I the person that can pick up extra shifts, take classes, and maintain a social life. Now, I get lucky if I can attend work more than three days each week. What started four years ago as anxiety, has turned into paranoia that my coworkers are out to get me fired from my job as an office clerk. Meanwhile, weekly panic attacks convince me that I am actively dying and have caused me to go to the E.R. on multiple occasions. Furthermore, two years ago I made the hard decision not to go into education because intrusive thoughts began to take over my headspace so that when working with children, I could not focus on anything other than worrying that they had been abused. Since then, I have taken low-stress jobs and the intrusive thoughts have taken the form of nonsensical phrases that take up space, but by-and-large, do not disturb me emotionally. Even though I have coping skills and medicine that help me manage a large barrage of symptoms, I am still doing twenty-four-seven symptom management and self-maintenance. This is not the craziness I was expecting. This is not the craziness I was warned about. This so-called craziness affects my life a lot more than it affects the lives of others.

Now I know that my grandma Maxine died because years of trauma and abuse led to an illness that was very hard for her to manage on her own, especially since the people that were supposed to care for her, isolated her. That illness caused delusions of persecution that prevented her from getting timely medical care. Abuse, partnered with mental illness, ultimately led to her demise. Today, I have removed the honorific, "crazy" from her name, validating her, and making her voice heard in places she could never imagine. I believe that is why I have inherited so many of Maxine's experiences. As her only granddaughter, I alone can finish her story. In my body I hold two lifetimes of abuse, gaslighting, and victim blaming, but my life will not continue those things. Within my relationships and sphere of influence, abuse will be addressed and negative stigmas will be challenged. By being vocal within my community about the challenges I face with schizophrenia and the abuse I have experienced, I can help end the stigmas that make people willing to abandon the mentally ill, or worse, blame them for violence. I share this story in order to help break the cycle of silence and stigma that still dominates the narrative in many families of schizophrenic individuals. I hope that somewhere, some family reading this will be able to respond to allegations of abuse or the development of mental illness by truly listening and supporting the loved one experiencing such horrors. I want to show people that we need empathy and people who believe in us for us to thrive.

Since her death, my grandma Maxine has left me a series of gifts that I have received as I have matured into adulthood, and in turn, I now gift her my life. She may have died from schizophrenia, but I am determined not to. Surviving the hell that we have shared is the love-letter I write to her. It tells her that I am grateful for her story, and that it has helped me to survive mine. It tells her that I love her. I believe that my life is the legacy Maxine would have wanted. Each day that I live is another page in my love letter to her; it's another day that I perpetuate Maxine's legacy.

Name of the Game – Julianne Keber (she/her)

SUSPECTS	Attempt #1	Attempt #2	Attempt #3	Attempt #4	Attempt #5
DYLAN				X	
FINN					X
BEAU	X				
CALEB			X		
CONNOR		X			

WEAPONS	Attempt #1	Attempt #2	Attempt #3	Attempt #4	Attempt #5
LACROSSE JACKET		X			
PHONE			X		
SNAPCHAT PICTURES					X
DIRECT MESSAGES				X	
BIKE	X				

ROOMS	Attempt #1	Attempt #2	Attempt #3	Attempt #4	Attempt #5
INDIANA			X		
BUMBLE APP				X	
FOURTH PERIOD		X			
DRIVEWAY	X				
BEDROOM					X

WHO SHATTERED JULIANNE'S SELF-WORTH?

I suggest it was Beau, with the bike, in the driveway.

She was only 13 years old when she laid eyes upon the perfect boy with the jet-black hair and dark brown eyes. With one glance, he had captured her heart and kept it locked away. It seemed impossible to her that she'd ever be worthy of his attention, but he proved her wrong and made her feel special each and every time he rode his bike over to her house after school. Her heart pounded and jumped for joy when she saw him in the driveway, waiting for her to come down. One small act had made her feel like the only girl in the world. Too bad his motive for doing so never matched with her fantasy.

I suggest it was Connor, with the lacrosse jacket, in fourth period.

He had a girlfriend, and she knew it. Despite that, she still allowed him to offer her multiple advances. She was desperate, and he knew it. The lacrosse jacket was only the beginning, but little did she know it was the beginning of the end. There she sat in class with the soft material draped over her freckled shoulders while multiple pairs of eyes burned holes in her back. One pair belonged to his best friend and the other belonged to the girl who should've been wearing the jacket; the girl who despised her with every ounce of her being.

I suggest it was Caleb, with the phone, in Indiana.

Even though she'd only been dating him for a month she had the rest of high school already planned out with him by her side. He'd be her first ever valentine, her date to the senior prom, and her partner-in-crime for life after graduation. She set her hopes higher than the clouds, but he managed to kick her off cloud nine and straight into the ground with one phone call. One conversation ended it all. He called from Indiana while away at his mom's because he couldn't manage the courage to do it face-to face. His cowardly act threw her into a downward spiral that would last for years to come.

I suggest it was Dylan, with the direct messages, in the Bumble app.

She had always believed there was more to guys than the desire for physical attraction, but he proved her wrong. He made her lose faith in humanity because he showed her what she'd never be: desirable and easy. She could never give him what he was looking for, and the worst part is that she wished she could. At the moment when he told her everything she'd wanted to hear and believe, she wanted nothing more than to be the kind of girl he was looking for. "What's the worst that could happen?" she thought, as she contemplated the opportunity. "Sacrifice," her subconscious whispered back.

I suggest it was Finn, with the Snapchat pictures, in the bedroom.

He tempted her, and she gave in. All she wanted was his attention and his affection and to gain it she had to give him what he wanted. She always knew the real reason people used the infamous picture app—the pictures were deleted and only seen briefly, even the worst pictures imaginable. Nobody but him would see them, so it couldn't hurt, right? Wrong. As far as she knew, his eyes were the only ones to see them, but it didn't change the fact that she exposed herself to gain a stranger's love. She sent him a piece of herself, and there was no way for her to ever get it back.

So, who did shatter Julianne's self-worth? Well, I'd say that's a trick question because there is no singular answer. In the end, all five culprits had a hand in demeaning the image she held of herself. Beau did ride his bike to see her more times than she could possibly count, but he was only doing so in an attempt to get to her best friend. Crack. Connor's motives are still unknown to this day, but one can assume he had a twisted sense of humor and only wanted to humiliate her. Crack. Caleb liked her quite a bit, of that she was certain, but she could never live up to the expectations set forth for him by his stepmother and his religion. Crack. Dylan wanted a one-night stand and even though she could never, ever be that girl, she'll always regret that she's not. Crack. Finn came across as different at first, but she soon found out that he and Dylan were birds of a feather, except she allowed him to take advantage. Crack. Little by little, each boy chipped away at her, leaving not only the broken shards in their wake, but the mutilated image of what she once was.

How To Craft a Hypochondriac — PQT (they/them)

Whether or not I'm a sociopath or narcissist is whichever wins me the argument.

It's a pithy joke, really. It's one of those jokes you earn the right to laugh at—the right to *make.* You say it to whoever will listen, you tip your head back, you laugh a quick, sharp laugh, the kind of laugh that doesn't *really* care, and you're an idiot if you ever think it did. You think about the fifteen-year-old trapped in a box with a window in it, frantically reaching out of it the only way they can to find the unmentionable *something* they know they are, and walking away every time, promising to do more later.

You forget about them, because you don't care, not really. And you're an idiot if you think you ever did.

Anyway.

I had a doctor's appointment the other day.

It doesn't matter when you read this; I would have had a doctor's appointment the other day regardless. Certain things fail a person.

What failed me came much sooner than most—my knees, my back, my brain.

I had a doctor's appointment the other day...

...and my doctor rushed me though as fast as he could.

...and my doctor told me to lose weight for the fourth time, even though I told her I was a recovering anorexic.

...and my doctor was kind, and took me seriously, and jumped straight to looking for unconventional answers.

...and my doctor laughed at my jokes, and that was about it.

Take your pick. They've all happened.

I had a doctor's appointment the other day, and they looked through my skin to the faultline itself, reached into me and drew out liquid evidence, looked at the tangible Something. And if none of them did that, I'd be able to grab their wrist and twist in a way arms didn't go; able to scream at them and demand care, just as I did to my mother.

I see my doctor...

...once every month.

...once every four months.

...only once so far, but that will change soon enough.

...as needed.

I don't see my doctors because they themselves have an unknowable Something that lets them peer into my very soul and know me better than I—or anyone around me—knows me. The matter of whether or not they think themselves to be blessed with empathetic superpowers is irrelevant; at the end of the day, their feelings mean just about as much as my abuser's when I moved away from her. I see my doctors because, put simply, they have a special machine they put my blood in, and that machine spits out empirical facts about my body.

Whether or not I'm a sociopath or narcissist depends on who I talk to, and who I talk to doesn't quite like sociopaths *or* narcissists very much.

In a sense, I get it. *Sociopath* and *narcissist* are dirty words; words with worlds of baggage strapped to each one, which the potential existence of could hurt not only you but anyone unfortunate enough to come into contact with you. But so is *cancer,* and we don't eschew diagnosing a tumor because the existence of it would make the people around you sad, much like how we don't unanimously pretend like a tumor leeches an unknowable Badness into your bloodstream, a badness separate from the illness it floods you with—an inherent moral badness that makes you turn on both the people you love and society itself, transforming you into a caricature of a person—a twisted thing which only exists to be the eternal villain, with no pity or justice afforded to you because the unknowable Badness of the tumor has corrupted you so much that it would do best for people, even doctors, to avoid you—nevermind the metastization slowly overtaking your body.

You're naked in therapy, with your legs spread wide open for the doctor to see, and only God knows if they'll stick a cotton swab in your unmentionables and call it a day or if they'll see the blindingly obvious problem and react the way you hoped they would.

And you're not God, no matter how much you wish you could be, because the only being safe from the mundane traumas inflicted by your fellow man is the Almighty Himself—you don't get to pick and choose what happens. All you're able to do is bare your most vulnerable parts to the world and hope they remain unviolated—I never got to pick; why should I afford you the privilege?

So, you're naked in therapy, but this time, there's no arm-twisting in the world that can save you from the plague of disinterest. There's no therapeutic equivalent to *I want it noted on my chart that you refused to run tests.* There are no objective truths in therapy, and the brain is much more fluid than most give it credit. What one therapist may think is sociopathy, another might think is narcissism. Another might think it's simply a trauma response, and another still might think it's a behavior not worth looking into. Some might take a patient's word of what is wrong with them into consideration—but most, at least when sociopaths are involved, tend to do the opposite.

I knew about my knees before I ever saw a doctor for them. Did you know that?

I had a brace with a donut around my knee. And the funny thing about it is—the funny thing is, at night, it wouldn't fit right. It wouldn't fit right, and no amount of adjusting would get it *to* fit. I figured, the brace must be moving, but the brace moves during the day, and I'm able to reorient it, so it must be—I said, age seventeen, alone in my bed—it must be my kneecap itself that moves. That's what I said, to no-one in particular, alone in a little box, with only a window to the outside.

My parents thought I was an idiot. Did you know that, too? They thought it was a fault of my own. *Just stretch,* they said, *and you will be fine.*

Did you know my doctor thought that, too?

Did you know that once I went to a specialist—and God knows my doctor didn't refer me, I went my damn self; blessings upon blessings, my insurance allowed it—he took an X-ray, and what did he see?

What did I see when he showed me it?

Two kneecaps, slant upon the side of my leg, tipped to the outsides in a way that would make anyone recoil in revulsion, phantom pains a fraction of my own overtaking their joints.

Did you know I thought I was a sociopath?

Did you know I thought myself a narcissist, too?

I just thought that was interesting.

You're naked in therapy again, and the person who decides what you look like underneath your clothes is not you.

You have a potbelly, extending past the waist of your pants, and fat that clings to your arms just after your shoulders. How could you ever have been anorexic?

Your hands aren't red from the slaps you've given your partner? Your throat not raw from endless upon endless discouragements? Your brain not filled to bursting with a bottomless catalog of the flaws and insecurities of everyone around you, ready to be turned against them like ammunition in a carefully crafted firearm? How could you ever be a narcissist, then? They're all abusive, haven't you heard? My mother was a narcissist, did you know that? My mother was a narcissist, and she said the most vile things to me—but you would never do that. You can't be a narcissist. You can't.

You haven't raped? You haven't raped serially? Are you not seeking help simply to avoid the judicial consequences of your rapes, as opposed to any real desire for help or—dare I say it—change? Then you're not a sociopath, not a *real* one, at least—what? You thought these ideas were only on the Internet? Of course not! Someone had to put them there, after all.

One of these was said to me by a licensed psychologist. One of these was said to someone else by a licensed psychologist. One of these was said by a layperson who was soon going to become a psychologist.

You don't get to pick and choose which options are best in your mind. You don't get to pretend I wasn't likened to a rapist by a professional, just as I don't get to forget that it happened.

You are naked at the doctor. You know you have cancer. You felt the hardened lump with your own two hands.

"My mother had cancer," your doctor emphatically explains, "and she was awful to me. She beat me, never paid attention to me, and told me how much of a burden I was to her."

"You're nice," the doctor says, her eyes as sincere as you've ever seen. "So you can't have cancer. It's not possible."

The MRI machine sits in the other room, unused.

"It's not possible."

Your skin is pristine, never having seen the prick of a needle.

"It can't be possible."

Inside of you, the tumor grows.

ABOUT THE CONTRIBUTORS

- A.J. Flora is a poet and musician currently living in North Carolina. His interests include bass guitar, animal rights, and rights for Southern people of color.

- Agnieszka Filipek is a Polish–born poet living in Ireland. Her work has been published worldwide. Her poems have appeared in *Amsterdam Quarterly, SAND Journal, Tilted House Review, Capsule Stories, Local Wonders Anthology, Lucent Dreaming, Black Bough Poetry, Crannóg, The Blue Nib, Chrysanthemum, Writing Home: The 'New Irish' Poets Anthology, Marble Poetry Magazine, Balloons Literary Journal*, and elsewhere. She has a poetry Facebook page dedicated to her writing at https://www.facebook.com/polmnieapoltobie

- Alexis Mitchell is an English teacher, author, and poet from New York. She began her writing journey at eight years old—from diaries with a lock and key to journals or random scribbles, writing has remained at the core of her existence. As of 2022, she has published 4 poetry collections: I Write, Therefore I Am, I Write Therefore I Am: Exposed, Hope Chest, and The Attic. Aside from teaching and writing, Alexis Mitchell can be found with her nose in a book or spending time with friends and family. Alexis Mitchell can be found on Instagram @_lexmwrites.

- Alice Baburek is an avid reader, determined writer and animal lover. She lives with her partner and three canine furry companions in northeast Ohio. Retired from one of the largest library systems in Ohio, she challenges herself to become an unforgettable emerging voice.

- Alice Carroll lives in the midwest and is a fiction and nonfiction content writer. Sometimes, she gets paid for it.

- Amy Devine is an artist from a lineage of artists whose poetry has been included in several publications including *Kitchen Table Quarterly* and *Mujer Manifesto*. She is based in Sydney, Australia and is currently working on her first book.

- Angela Acosta (she/her) is a bilingual Latina poet and scholar from Florida. She won the 2015 Rhina P. Espaillat Award from West Chester University and her poems have appeared in *Panochazine, Pluma, Toyon Literary Magazine*, and *Latinx Audio Lit Mag*. She is currently completing her Ph.D. in Iberian Studies at The Ohio State University where she studies the lives and works of early twentieth century Spanish women writers.

- Anita Howard is a writer, storyteller and actor living in Passage West, Co. Cork, Ireland. Her work features in *HeadStuff, Poetica Review, Bluepepper* and the *Don't Get Caught!* anthology by Write In 4 Charity, Leicester, also the *Zooanthology* by Sweetycat Press. She is on Twitter as @AnitaHowardSto1.

- Ant is a 20 year old living in Scotland. They are studying English

- April Renee is a chronically ill and therefore chronically underemployed poet. Though still relatively inexperienced in the professional world, April has been writing poetry for over 15 years and harbors a great passion for the craft. Through her poetry, April explores the intersections of her identities as a disabled, queer woman of the lower class. The 25-year-old currently resides in Portland, Oregon with her partner, three pets, and a myriad of neglected plants.

- B. Lynn Carter was born and raised in the Bronx. She earned a degree in creative writing from The City College of New York. Lynn's debut novel "Jus Breathe," published by Between the Lines Publications, is scheduled to launch on October 11th 2022. An excerpt from "The Eyes Have It," her, as yet unpublished, second book, has won first place in the fiction category of The Black Writers Workshop's 2022 'Chapter One' writing competition. She's also had short stories published in several literary magazines. Her short story "One Wild Ride," which appeared in Aaduna magazine was nominated for the Pushcart award in 2014. Lynn's short story "Las Sinverguenzas" originally appeared in the Drunk Monkeys literary magazine in 2012.

- Benjamin Eric's stories have been featured in *New Plains Review, East by Northeast, Prometheus Dreaming*, and has upcoming fiction pieces that will appear in *On The Run* and *Suburban Witchcraft Magazine*. Previously, he was a member of the The Washington DC Comedy Writers Group. He lives in Washington DC, where he was born and raised, with his wife, Dana, and their 80-pound dog, Appa.

- Ben Umayam moved to NYC to write the Great American Filipino Gay Short Story. He worked for political pollsters, then became a fancy hotel chef and then retired and moved to Colorado. He is working that short story again. He was published most recently by *The Midway Journal, BULL, The Phare, Down in the Dirt, Blue Pepper, Metaworker*, and others.

- Beth Macdonald has a degree in anthropology and over 20 years of professional experience as a non-profit executive creating communities of belonging. She uses her passion for religion, myth, and genealogy along with a distinct (and witty) feminist viewpoint to tell stories and ask questions about what it means to belong to ourselves, our families, and the places we live. You can often find her musing around on Instagram @tiny_distractions.

- Bett Butler's (she, her, hers) poetry, videos, and short fiction have appeared in small-press publications in the U.S., U.K., E.U., and Canada. An award-winning songwriter and jazz musician, she co-owns Mandala Music Production in San Antonio, Texas, where she and bassist/composer Joël Dilley produce music and spoken word licensed for HBO, Discovery Channel, and more.

- Braden Hofeling is an emerging poet located in Portland, Oregon. He has two self-published collections of poetry out and is hoping to publish his third book through an independent small press. His work has been featured in the *Gival press ArLiJo issue 153 journal, Death Rattle's Penrose Vol. 2, Prometheus Dreaming, Arc Prose magazine* and *New Note poetry*.

- Caitlin Gemmell (she/her) is a tea drinking, countryside dwelling, potion making poet and witch. She founded #enchantedsimplicity on Instagram, and has had her poems published in *Rue Scribe, One Sentence Poems,* and *Minison Project Zine*. A selection of her fairy tale poems is included in a forthcoming, as yet untitled, anthology.

- Candi Martin is a music and nature lover from the UK. She recently completed MA Creative Writing and Wellbeing, delivering free workshops for keyworkers online through the Pandemic. Publications with South Bank Poetry, MONO Fiction, Fragmented Voices and others. Instagram: @candi_says_

- Carella is a poet and digital artist who splits her time between the ethereal world of dreams, and Toronto, Canada, depending on the weather. Her work involves themes of mental health, nature and sexuality, often in a surrealist tone. Carella is the recipient of the Stanley Fefferman Prize in Creative Writing (2006) and 2nd place winner in the Open Minds Quarterly BrainStorm Poetry Contest (2017). Recently, she has been published in Margins Magazine, Wrongdoing Magazine, Shuf Poetry and Myth & Lore. Forthcoming publications include Paddler Press, Solstice Literary Magazine, Fragmented Voices, Writeresque and Stripes Literary Magazine.

- Carla M. Cherry is a high school English teacher. Her poetry has appeared in various publications, including *Random Sample Review, MemoryHouse, Bop Dead City, Anti-Heroin Chic, 433, Raising Mothers* and has been nominated for Best of the Net. Her books of poetry, *Gnat Feathers and Butterfly Wings, Thirty Dollars and a Bowl of Soup, Honeysuckle Me, These Pearls Are Real,* and *Stardust and Skin* are available via iiPublishing. She has an M.F.A. in Creative Writing from the City College of New York.

- Carole Greenfield grew up in Colombia and lives in Massachusetts, where she teaches in a public elementary school. In the previous century, her work appeared in *Red Dancefloor, Gulfstream, Women's Words: Resolution* and *The Sow's Ear*. More recently, her work can be seen in *Beltway Poetry Quarterly, Eunoia Review, Sparks of Calliope, Autumn Sky Daily Poetry, Glacial Hills Review* and *Sky Island Journal. Eve* first appeared in *Eunoia Review*.

- Charles K. Carter (he/him) is a queer poet from Iowa. He holds an MFA from Lindenwood University. His poems have appeared in several literary journals. He is the author of Read My Lips (*David Robert Books,* November 2022) and several chapbooks. He can be found on Twitter and Instagram @CKCpoetry.

- Christian Ryan Ram Malli has a degree in creative writing from the University of Santo Tomas. During his stay, his poetry was awarded multiple times in the annual Gawad Ustetika. He is now a content writer based in Metro Manila, Philippines. He has won several poetry slams contests, including the Tanghal-Makata slam at the Cultural Center of the Philippines. His short poetry suite, Kween Among Men, also won at the Normal Awards for Gender-Inclusive Literature. He was a fellow of the

5th Amelia Lapeña-Bonifacio Writers Workshop. His works have appeared in Points of Contact, Dx Machina: Philippine Literature in the Time of COVID-19, Cordite Poetry Review, Queer Southeast Asia, among others.

- Cristy Shaner is an actress and writer based in New York City, and a recent graduate of Stella Adler's Professional Conservatory. She has performed in theatre productions in Chicagoland and New York City. When she's not writing or acting, Cristy spends most of her time obsessing over her cat, knitting, and watching horror movies.

- Cruz Sanchez is an aspiring writer who grew up in rural Idaho. He aims to write prices that have impact on readers and express his own emotions. Outside of work you can find him play with his dog, reading and playing guitar to himself on rainy days.

- Dana Kinsey is an actor and teacher published in *Writers Resist, Fledgling Rag, Drunk Monkeys, ONE ART, On the Seawall, Porcupine Literary, Sledgehammer Lit, West Trestle Review, Autumn Sky Poetry Daily,* and *Prose Online.* Dana's play, *WaterRise,* was produced at the Gene Frankel Theatre. Her chapbook, *Mixtape Venus,* is published by *I. Giraffe Press*. Visit wordsbyDK.com

- Daniel is a poet from Neath, South Wales, UK. After life was turned upside down by his ongoing battle with severe M.E., he rediscovered his passion for poetry that had been dormant since his teenage years. Writing has served as a distraction from his struggles ever since. Daniel has been acclaimed by numerous poetry competitions, including those hosted by: Oliver Goldsmith Literature Festival, Wine Country Writers Festival, Ohio Poetry Day, Westmoreland Arts & Heritage Festival, Utah State Poetry Society, and Jurica-Suchy Nature Museum.Daniel has also had poetry published by *The Society of Classical Poets* and *The Black Cat Poetry Press.*

- DC Diamondopolous is an award-winning short story, and flash fiction writer with hundreds of stories published internationally in print and online magazines, literary journals, and anthologies. DC's stories have appeared in: *Progenitor, 34th Parallel, So It Goes: The Literary Journal of the Kurt Vonnegut Museum and Library, Lunch Ticket,* and others. DC's recently released collection *Captured Up Close (20th Century Short-Short Stories)* has two Pushcart Prize nominated stories and one nominated for Best of the Net Anthology. Her first collection of stories was *Stepping Up.* She lives on the California coast with her wife and animals.

- Dee Allen is an African-Italian performance poet based in Oakland, California. Active on creative writing & Spoken Word since the early 1990s. Author of 7 books--*Boneyard, Unwritten Law, Stormwater, Skeletal Black* [all from POOR Press], *Elohi Unitsi* [Conviction 2 Change Publishing] and 2 his newest, *Rusty Gallows: Passages Against Hate* [Vagabond Books] and *Plans* [Nomadic Press] and 60 anthology appearances under his figurative belt so far.

- Dixie Kootz-Eades was born and raised in the mountains of Idaho, then moved to Kansas for college where she received her Bachelor's degree in Biblical studies. She has since changed career paths, now trying to establish herself as an author after completing several Graduate level classes in English Literature and Teaching English as a Second Language. She identifies as a later-in-life lesbian and lives in Kansas City with her polycule and their cats.

- Dorothy Johnson-Laird is a poet, social worker, and activist who lives in New York City. She received an M.F.A in creative writing from Sarah Lawrence College. Dorothy also has a passion for African music. She has published music journalism with www.afropop.org and www.worldmusiccentral.org. Recent poems were accepted for publication by *Evening Street Review, BeZine, Soul-Lit journal*, and *Aji*, among others. More of Dorothy's poetry can be found at: https://www.facebook.com/Dorothy-Johnson-Laird-Poet-106451582140735

- Eaton Jackson is a Jamaican, naturalized US citizen. He has been writing all of his adult life, now a much older person, he is still on the learning curve, with an undying desire to produce publishable works. A few pieces of his writings have appeared in various publications (Scarlet Leaf Review, River Poet magazine, The New Verse). Eaton's dream is to be read as a credible writer.

- Ed Ahern resumed writing after forty odd years in foreign intelligence and international sales. He's had four hundred stories and poems published so far, and six books. Ed works the other side of writing at *Bewildering Stories*, where he sits on the review board and manages a posse of nine review editors. He's also lead editor at *The Scribes Micro Fiction* magazine.

- Ms. Kirkpatrick-Vrenios resides in Mendocino, CA. Twice nominated for a Pushcart Prize, her poetry has been featured in such online poetry columns as: *Ekphrastic Review, Abyss and Apex, The American Journal of Poetry, Kentucky Review, Form Quarterly, Scissors and Spackle, Folliate Oak* and in issues of *Poeming Pigeon, Unsplendid* and *The Edison Review*. Her prize-winning chapbook, *Special Delivery* was published by *Yellow Chair Press*, and her second chapbook, *Empty the Ocean with a Thimble*, by *Word Tech Communications*. A Professor Emerita from American University, she has performed as a solo singing artist across Europe and the United States.

- Elsie Dimaandal is a 45-year-old aspiring writer from Batangas City, Philippines. While having an affair with books, she is taking care of her beloved 91-year-old mother.

- Émilie Galindo is a French millennial who specialises in 1960s American pop culture & loves cranking up the volume on subtext by using surrealism and/or magical realism. Citrus-Lover. Paisley-head. Forever between two binges or between two Dylan songs. You can also find her work in *Flare Journal, Dead Skunk Mag, The Literary Canteen, Penumbra Journal*, and *orangepeel*.

- Eric Abalajon is currently a lecturer at the University of the Philippines Visayas, Iloilo. His works have appeared in *Ani, Katitikan, Loch Raven Review, Cha: An Asian Literary Journal, The Tiger Moth Review, Dx Machina*, and elsewhere. Recently his poems are included in the collections *Sobbing in Seafood City (Sampaguita Press,*

2022) and *Footprints: An Anthology of New Ecopoetry* (Broken Sleep Books, 2022). He lives near Iloilo City.

- Eric Knowlson is a writer and poet hailing from Albuquerque, NM. He is fascinated by the fleeting moments of beauty that only last seconds, but shape lives forever. He attempts to capture these transient moments in his writing. His work has appeared in *The Leonardo, Coffin Bell Journal*, and *The Dillydoun Review*. He was a reader for *Blue Mesa Review's* 41stedition. He teaches Special Education at Albuquerque Public Schools and is currently enrolled in an MFA program at Albertus Magnus College. He's excited to share his work and connect with other writers. He's always open to correspondence. Send him an email at Etknowlson@gmail.com.

- Evan Violets, is a lofi-loving soul who strings his dreams and thoughts into more literary expressions. His more specific passion lies in stringing together fragments of imagery to assemble an envisionable scene in audience' minds. Whilst adventurous at experimenting with literary concepts, he isn't the best at experimenting in chemistry.

- Fatima Riaz is 18 years old being whose poetry is muddled in misty stillness and whose words are like birds that loved to soar but their fluttering has long ago ebbed away. She, with her waning ocean of thoughts and melting intuition, speaks through mere poems that reflect the lucidity and sagacity of her soul. You can find her on Instagram as @im_fatimariaz

- G.F. Sage is a 22-year-old lesbian poet based in New England. Being both a voice and an advocate for survivors of abuse, her words offer healing to not only herself but to many others. Her poems have appeared in *Celestite Poetry*, and in *Sunday Mornings at the River*. Her debut poetry collection is forthcoming with *Querencia Press*. For more visit www.gfsage.com or @gf_sage on Instagram.

- Gina Bowen lives, breathes, and photographs the mountains of Eastern Tennessee. She spends her time writing on her porch and getting lost in the woods with her pups. Her work has been published in a variety of anthologies and magazines. More from Gina can be found on Instagram, at the handle @ivy.haunts

- Greg Sendi is a native Detroiter who lives in and writes from the Rogers Park neighborhood of Chicago where, according to a recent headline, only the weird survive. His career has included poetry, fiction, essays, and short plays as well as broadcast and trade journalism. In the early 1990s, he served as fiction editor of *Chicago Review*. Most recently, his work has appeared or been accepted for publication in a number of literary magazines and online outlets, including *Apricity, Beyond Words Literary Magazine, The Briar Cliff Review, Burningword Literary Journal, Clarion, Coffin Bell, CONSEQUENCE, Flashes of Brilliance, Great Lakes Review, The Headlight Review, The Masters Review, New American Legends, Plume, Pulp Literature, San Antonio Review, Sparks of Calliope*, and *upstreet*.

- Hayden Kasal-Barsky is a sophomore, currently attending the University of Hawaii at Manoa. She's studying Elementary Education and Special Education but dreams of becoming an international poet and traveling the world to inspire others (especially in underdeveloped areas) to read and love poetry. Hayden has recited her poems at a few marches including "March For Our Lives" and an earth day event. She's currently publishing a short anthology called "An Ode To My Fellow Sisters" and is being featured in another poetry anthology. Outside of school and poetry Hayden enjoys making new friends, taking photos, and being involved in humanitarian projects.

- Helen Parker is a poet from the UK, who has been writing for 2 decades on Friday nights to keep herself sane whilst starting and selling businesses— she is now Managing Director for a groundbreaking Creative Podcast Agency, whilst also training in law. "Wood Queens" was written after witnessing a close friend bravely prosecuting an abusive relative as an adult. She is a romantic who has been with her husband for 25 years, her closest friends for longer, and someone who believes in good people, the strength of women, and the beauty and power of words to make the world a better place.

- Herb Nathans is a native of Southern California and an emerging writer and poet. He is currently exploring the psychology of virtual reality via novel format. In his spare time, he enjoys computer programming, gardening, exploring the city and rocking out.

- Howie Good is a poet and collage artist on Cape Cod. His latest poetry books are *Famous Long Ago* (Laughing Ronin Press) and *The Bad News First* (Kung Fu Treachery Press).

- Iwuagwu Ikechukwu is an African poet, Essayist, Screenwriter and Dramatist whose poems, reviews and short stories have appeared in several literary magazines across the world both online and in print. His short story "Five Shades of Victory" was a recipient of an honourable mention in the IHRAF Creators of Justice award in New York - 2020 edition, he was also shortlisted for the 2022 Alpine Fellowship Visual Arts Prize in London, UK. When he is not writing, he can be found researching, teaching or reading the works of Christopher Okigbo, Isidore Diala, Soyinka, Adichie, Buchi Emecheta & Ifesinachi Nwadike. His publications "The Baptism (A collection of Three Short Stories)", " After Dusk Comes Dawn", "See History" & "Shakespeare Speaks Pidgin" are available on Amazon.

- Iris Leona Marie Cross started writing short nonfiction stories in 2019. She was Gotham Writers 25-word story winner July 2020, Preservation Foundation's Creative Nonfiction Contest finalist 2020 and 2021, and LIGHT Public Health Writing Contest second place winner June 2022.

- James Piatt is a twice nominated Best of the Web nominee and three time Pushcart nominee and has had five poetry books "The Silent Pond," (2012), "Ancient Rhythms," (2014), "LIGHT," (2016),"Solace Between the Lines," (2019), and Serenity (2022), over 1735 poems, five novels, seven essays, and 35 short stories published worldwide, in over 258 publications. He earned his doctorate from BYU, and his BS and MA from California State Polytechnic University, SLO.

- Janet M. Powers, Professor Emerita at Gettysburg College, has published poetry in many small journals. Her chapbook, *Difficult to Subdue as the Wind*, appeared in 2009. This old lady still stands with signs on street corners trying to make sense of our sorry world.

- Javier Sandoval was born in Mexico's Chihuahuan Desert, but later grew up in Texas (falling for its blues music) and in North Carolina (living in a shelter for three years). After building a startup invested in by Microsoft, he studied Comp Sci and Lit Arts at Brown University on its full-ride Leadership Endowed Award, co-authored "2 Billion Under 20" (St. Martin's Press), and published his first book of fiction, a literary gang-thriller, "Cicada, Ladybug" (Thought Catalog Books). He is now pursuing an MFA in Creative Writing at the University of Alabama. You can follow him on IG for updates and jokes @JavierWantsCandy.

- Jill P. Strachan is an emerging writer living in Washington, DC. Her career in arts and association management spanned 40 years. She holds a PhD from Syracuse University. She published *Waterfalls, The Moon and Sensible Shoes-One Lesbian Life* in October 2021. Using letters and diaries from six decades, the author ties disparate family life and American post-war life together, while providing a personal account of one Lesbian life emerging in the 1970s to the AIDS crisis and beyond.

- Jillian Calahan (she/her/they) is a poet and short story writer from Seattle, Washington. When she's not writing you can find her in a bookstore, chilling with her 4 cats and 2 dogs, crafting, or taking too many pictures of pretty sunsets. You can find her work on Instagram @novamarie_poetry

- Jo was born in 1996 and currently lives in Zürich, Switzerland. They are constantly searching and working on ways to shape their own voice to be able to express themselves and the home within them. They published their first collection *Primary Poems* in 2020. Fun Facts: they love broccolis and are terrified by grasshoppers.

- Joan McNerney's poetry has been included in numerous literary magazines worldwide. She has four Best of the Net nominations. Her latest titles are *The Muse in Miniature, Love Poems for Michael*, and *At Work* all available on Amazon.

- Jodie Oakes is a poet living between a rusty transit van and a rural village in Bulgaria. After taking an unplanned break from creative work over the last few years, she is back to explore modern themes of quiet rage, survivorship, and rebirth. Her work has previously been published in *the Emerge Literary Journal, Fire, Moodswing, The Global Tapestry Journal, Maybles Labels*, and various anthologies. She is currently working on her second chapbook.

- Over the past 30 years John Barr's poems have been published in five books, four fine press editions, and many magazines, including *The New York Times, Poetry*, and others. He was also the Inaugural President of the Poetry

Foundation. His newest book, *The Boxer of Quirinal*, will be published by Red Hen Press in June 2023. You can view more of his work at johnbarrpoetry.com and on Instagram (@johnbarrpoetry).

- Jordan Nishkian is an Armenian-Portuguese writer based in California. Her prose and poetry explore themes of duality and have been featured in national and international publications. She is the Editor-in-Chief of Mythos literary magazine and author of *Kindred*, a novella.

- Josephine Raye Kelly is a queer writer smitten by the redwoods. After obtaining their Master's of Social Work from Cal State East Bay in 2022, they co-founded Ouch!, a queer art collective based in the San Francisco Bay Area. Josephine's words are featured or forthcoming in The Spotlong Review, beestung, Chinquapin Literary Magazine and elsewhere.

- Julianne Keber is a senior at the University of North Carolina at Charlotte. She is majoring in English and hopes to enter into the publishing industry once she graduates. In her spare time, she thoroughly enjoys reading and writing. She mostly writes poetry and shares it through her Instagram account @juliannekeber.

- Karen Carter, a veteran teacher in post-secondary and secondary education, teaches high school English in North Carolina. She holds a PhD from Emory University, Atlanta, Georgia. Her poems have appeared in *Avalon Literary Review, Broadkill Review, Cathexis Northwest Press, Eclectica, MacGuffin, Miller's Pond, Poetry Quarterly, The Write Launch, Tiny Seed Literary Journal*, and *Wild Roof Journal. Kenyon Review* awarded her as a teacher/poet a writer's workshop taught by renowned US poet laureate Tracy K. Smith.

- Kate MacAlister is an author, feminist activist and bio-medical scientist. Her works have been published in journals and anthologies all over the world. Her poems are stories of human connection and the dreams of revolution. Coffee, her cat Bella, and her feminist friends are particularly important for her creative process. Find Kate on Instagram @kissed.by_fire

- Katherine Leonard grew up in the US and Italy. She lived in Massachusetts at the time of John F Kennedy's assassination and experienced segregation and Martin Luther King, Jr.'s assassination as a high school student in rural Texas. She has been a chemist, a geologist, and an oncology nurse/nurse practitioner. Her work has been previously published in literary journals, including *Sonora Review, Hole in the Head Review, Speckled Trout Review, FERAL*, and *Tipping the Scales*. Her work is upcoming, *Allium* and *Central Texas Writers Society Anthology*.

- Katja Warren Wild writes feral, unruly, deeply earthy poetry. Words woven with nettle fibres, moonlight on spider webs, and rusty old nails. Poems with teeth, claws and hairy armpits. Poems that menstruate and cry and dance at their own funeral. Poems that laugh in the face of anyone who takes themselves too seriously. Find Katja on instagram @katjawarrenwild

- Keely Quinn has been writing poetry since she was young, but just recently found the words and courage to call herself a poet. As an exvangelical, her poetry often reflects the fight against the church she was raised in and the damage it caused her as she began to find herself in adulthood.

- Ken Been's perceptions about the human experience were magnified when he became a grandfather, a milestone that offers a second chance to observe how lives develop and what happens along the way. His poetry has appeared in *Plainsongs, Poetica Magazine, Speckled Trout Review, Kestrel, Remembering Lawrence Ferlinghetti* (anthology), *Passages North* and elsewhere.

- Ken Cathers has a B.A. from the University of Victoria and a M.A. from York University in Toronto. He has been published in numerous periodicals, anthologies as well as seven books of poetry, most recently Letters From the Old Country with *Ekstasis Press*. His work has appeared in publications in Canada, the United States, Australia, Ireland, and Africa. He has recently published work in *Platoès Cave, Zoetic Press , The McGuffin*, and the *Remington Review*. He has a chapbook forthcoming from broke press in Canada and a full-length poetry book from *Impspired Press* in England later this year.

- Kevin Brown has published two short story collections, *Death Roll* and *Ink On Wood*, and has had Fiction, Non-fiction and Poetry published in over 200 Literary Journals, Magazines and Anthologies. He won numerous writing competitions, fellowships, and grants, and was nominated for multiple prizes and awards, including three *Pushcart Prizes*.

- Kristin H. Sample's fiction has appeared in *Running Wild, The Dead Mule School of Southern Literature, Sand Hills, Mawth*, and more. Her essays have been published in the *New York Times*, the *Washington Post*, and *Parents* magazine. Her debut novel North Shore South Shore was one of the first kickstarter successes for fiction. She holds two advanced degrees in English from Fordham University. She lives in Dallas, TX with her family. Follow her on twitter/IG: @kristinsample or visit her website kristinsample.com.

- Laura Holt Andersen is a poet who's always wearing noticeable gold jewelry to add shine to the life she likes to write about. She has both Danish and English poems published in magazines. In her everyday life, mostly spent in gardens, she works with writing in all kinds of ways, and is always thinking in rhyme.

- Laura Theis writes in her second language. Her work appears in *Poetry, Mslexia, Rattle, Strange Horizons, Asimov's, Aesthetica*, etc. A Forward Prize nominee and AM Heath Prize recipient, as well as the winner of the Oxford Brookes Poetry Prize, the Mogford Short Story Prize, and the Hammond House International Literary Award, she was runner-up for both of the 2021 Mairtin Crawford Awards, shortlisted for the Alpine Fellowship Writing Prize, and a finalist for several other awards including the BBC Short Story Award and the UK National Poetry Competition in two consecutive years. Her debut 'how to extricate yourself' won the Brian Dempsey Memorial Prize, was nominated for an Elgin Award and chosen as an Oxford Poetry Library Book of the Month.

- Lev Verlaine is a trans poet based in Washington State.

- Lin Flores (she/they) lives and works in SLC, UT as a full-time poet and creative writing student. They are enrolled in the online Creative Writing Masters Program at the University of New Orleans. Lin published her first chapbook, *Reflections While Living in Utah*, in 2020. This work quickly became a local bestseller, making it the most sold book at Utah's first LBGTQ bookstore—Under The Umbrella. When Flores isn't coaching high school poetry slam, she is volunteering her time at Encircle, an LGBTQ resource center in SLC. Flores loves art, music, history, donuts, and God.

- Native New Yorker, LindaAnn LoSchiavo, a Pushcart Prize, Rhysling Award, Best of the Net, and Dwarf Stars nominee, is a member of SFPA, The British Fantasy Society, and The Dramatists Guild. Elgin Award winner "A Route Obscure and Lonely," "Concupiscent Consumption," "Women Who Were Warned," and "Messengers of the Macabre" by Audience Askew [October 2022] are her latest poetry titles. Up next: a tombstone-heavy collection in hardcover by Beacon Books. She has been leading a poetry critique group for two years. Her Texas Guinan film won "Best Feature Documentary" at N.Y. Women's Film Fest (Dec. 2021).

- Linda M. Crate's works have been published in numerous magazines and anthologies both online and in print. She is the author of eleven published chapbooks, four full-lengths, and three micro-chaps. She has a novella, also, called *Mates* (Alien Buddha Publishing, March 2022).

- Louise Kim is a Korean American student at the Horace Mann School in The Bronx, NY. Their writing has been published in a number of publications, including *Brown Sugar Lit, Green Ink Poetry, Gypsophila Zine, The WEIGHT Journal,* and *Panoply Zine*. Her work has been nationally recognized by the Scholastic Art and Writing Awards and the National High School Poetry Contest.

- Lucia Cherciu writes both in English and in Romanian and is the author of five books of poetry, including *"Train Ride to Bucharest"* (Sheep Meadow Press), a winner of the Eugene Paul Nassar Poetry Prize. She is the 2021-2022 Dutchess County Poet Laureate, and her work was nominated three times for a Pushcart Prize and twice for Best of the Net. She teaches English at SUNY/Dutchess.

- Lucia Coppola is an ESL teacher who is originally from New York and has lived in France and California. She has a professional background in dance and body techniques. Her writing is informed by nature and traditional storytelling. Some of her work has been read on the radio and published online and in print. Her poetry collection "Talking With Trees" has recently been published with *Plants and Poetry*.

- Maegen McAuliffe O'Leary is a poet and mother from the Pacific Northwest. Her work focuses on the intersection of feminism, motherhood, marriage, magic, and the human body and its place in nature. Her chapbook, Bodies to Bury the Hunger, is forthcoming from Bottlecap Press. She studied creative writing at the University of Washington, holds a bachelor's degree in Liberal Arts from The Evergreen State College, and a Master's degree in Irish Studies from the National University of Ireland Galway. Her selected poetry can also be read on Instagram @m.f.mca. She currently works in communications for a non-profit corporation dedicated to water quality and conservation, but she would love to quit her job to write poetry and talk to the crows.

- Maggie Kaprielian (she/her) is a seventeen-year-old from Maryland. She is an editor in chief for the *Erewhon Literary Arts Magazine* and president of Potomac's chapter of the Maryland Teen Writers Association. She attended Susquehanna University's Summer Poetry Workshops in 2021 and 2022.

- Margaret D. Stetz is the Mae and Robert Carter Professor of Women's Studies and Professor of Humanities at the University of Delaware. She has spent most of her life in academia, but still finds it hard to reconcile that with the world she knew as a working-class child in Queens, New York. Many of her poems reflect this class-based tension and disjunction. Recently, her poetry has appeared in *A Plate of Pandemic, C*nsorship Magazine, Kerning, Mono, Review Americana, Rushing Thru the Dark, West Trestle Review, Existere, Azure*, and other journals, as well in the *Washington Post*.

- Marianna Pizzini Mankle is a Montana native who now calls Nebraska home. She has an MA in Communication from Arizona State University. Her writing can be found in Kiosk, Calla Press, Writeresque Literary Magazine, Spoonie Journal, New Note Poetry, and more. She can be found watching reality TV with her husband when she isn't writing.

- Marija Rakić Mimica was born in 1982 in Split. She graduated in Croatian language and literature and comparative literature at the Faculty of Philosophy in Zagreb. She has won four literary awards for her short stories; Prose for the best prose manuscript by an author under 35 for 2015, Brod knjižara Brod kulture 2016, third prize in the competition Story in the City of Trogir City Library, first prize for prose in the Literary Competition "Ticket 2020". So far, she has published prose in all major literary magazines. Short stories were also published in the collections 20 + 1 The Most Beautiful Story for Summer published by Brod kulture, in the finals of Lapis Histriae 2014, the finals of the Zlatko Tomičić Award 2018, the Bedekovčina 2015 collection. She published a collection of short stories Dancing in the Yard .). She is currently the leader of a drama workshop at the Sunce moje malo Kindergarten and the Book Lovers' Club at the Peristil House of Culture and Language in Split. She is employed in Split as a Croatian language teacher in high school.

- Mary Dooty is a self-taught poet from Iowa. She loves painting, expressing feelings through writing, black cats, and green tea. She hopes to one day get her masters in English and publish her own book.

- Maryam Imogen Ghouth is of Saudi Arabian, Iranian, and British origin and lives in Dubai, where she makes poetry films that explore psychological themes such as existential crises. Her series "Journey of Becoming" was showcased in Dubai's arthouse cinema, Akil, and her poems were narrated in short films such as "Under the Sun," which premiered worldwide. Her most recent work focuses on written poetry, deriving inspiration from nature and science, with her latest published in *The Poet Anthology, Last Leaves, inScribe*, and *Vita Brevis Anthology*, among others.

- Megan Diedericks is an avid writer. Her debut poetry collection, "the darkest of times, the darkest of thoughts" is available on Amazon. She is situated in South Africa and is proudly part of the LGBTQ+ community. More information is available here, https://megwrites.carrd.co/

- Mia-Jo Feeley (she/her) A student, poet, and member of the Amplify Tulsa Youth Leadership Council. Her work is meant to inspire fellow trans people to take up space without compromise. When she isn't writing, you can find her on the edges of the pit at punk shows or getting lost in the woods.

- Mimi Flood has been published in *Dark Thirty Poetry Publishing, Querencia press, The Graveyard zine, Scar Tissue Magazine*, and *Gypsophila*. You can find her on Instagram Marigold_Jesus and Tumblr Marigoldjesus.tumblr.com.

- Nelly Shulman is a writer currently based in Berlin. Her work has appeared on JewishFiction.net, in the Vine Leaves Press Anthology of the Best 2021 Flash Fiction and in various literary magazines. She is a winner of two writing awards.

- Nicholas Barnes earned a Bachelor of Arts in English at Southern Oregon University. He is currently working as an editor in Portland, and enjoys music, museums, movie theaters, and rain. His least favorite season is summer. His favorite soda is RC Cola.

- Nissa Valdez is a poet, writer, gardener, and a student of the natural world. She is a wife and mother who believes in the importance of story, listening to one another, and the power of beauty. Nissa is from Minneapolis, MN where she has had a practice as a bodyworker and holistic esthetician for over twenty years.

- Nweke Benard Okechukwu is a Nigerian poet. He writes from Onitsha in Anambra State where he's an undergraduate in Mass Communication at Nnamdi Azikiwe University, Awka. His works have appeared/are forthcoming in *West Trade Review, New Yorker, Isele, Epoch*, & elsewhere. His Twitter & Instagram handles are @romeobenokechukwu.

- Ocean (she/they) is a Black-British writer born in London with Ghanaian and Nigerian heritage. She is currently studying Psychology as an undergraduate and works part-time in an independent bookshop where she enjoys being surrounded by books from all over the world. Ocean also runs children's workshops, called Adanko Workshops, to introduce children to literature from all over Africa and hopes to use her writing and experiences to aid in anti-racism practices.

- Patty Somlo's most recent book, *Hairway to Heaven Stories,* was published by Cherry Castle Publishing, a Black-owned press committed to literary activism. *Hairway* was a Finalist in the American Fiction Awards and Best Book Awards. Two of Somlo's previous books, *The First to Disappear* (Spuyten Duyvil) and *Even When Trapped Behind Clouds: A Memoir of Quiet Grace* (WiDo Publishing), were Finalists in several book contests. Her work has appeared in *Guernica, Gravel, Sheepshead Review, Under the Sun,* the *Los Angeles Review, and The Nassau Review,* among others, and in over 30 anthologies. She received Honorable Mention for Fiction in the Women's National Book Association Contest, was a Finalist in the Parks and Points Essay Contest and in the J.F. Powers Short Fiction Contest, had an essay selected as Notable for Best American Essays, and has been nominated for the Pushcart Prize multiple times, as well as to Best of the Net.

- *Paytience Ferguson is a Graphic designer and Visual artist who was born in Kentucky but now based in Vancouver. Their work often explores the relationship between art and trauma, what started as a personal journey ended in them embedding all aspects of mental health and the unknown into their work. When the Rembrandt medallion holder is not creating art, they are caught writing short stories and poetry or their nose buried in books. Her dream is to be able to be a full time artist illustrating for writers alongside her cat.*

- PQT may or may not have something deeply wrong with them—the jury's still out on that one. Regardless, they enjoy writing about things nobody quite expects, but which latches in their brains forever, and long walks off a short pier. Occasional mad ramblings can be found @peektea on Twitter.

- Prathami is a queer kid from Bangalore, India, and their work revolves around confessional and imagist themes. Their poems have been published in *Free Verse Revolution, Under the Basho, Failed Haiku,* and *Zenerations,* among others.

- Rachel Rose holds a Masters degree in German language and literature from the University of Illinois at Urbana-Champaign. She writes pieces seeking to raise awareness regarding women's issues and domestic abuse. She currently resides in Madison, WI with her cat, Colleen.

- Renee Chen is an Asian-American writer. She has been published in the *Daphne Review,* the *Wilderness House Literary Review,* and elsewhere. As an addict to detective and mystery fiction, she can be found reading Agatha Christie and Conan Doyle when she is not writing!

- Currently attending university, Rye Owen is a writer who follows their passions into the realms of LGBTQ and fantasy.

- Sabrynne Buchholz is a creative soul with a particular interest in poetry. Sabrynne is also an accomplished artist and musician. You can find her chasing tarantulas, reading over a cup of tea, and spending time with her family, friends, and three young Italian Greyhounds who keep the family on their toes!

- Sally Quon is a writer and photographer, rediscovering her voice after a long confinement. She has been published in numerous anthologies, including "Voicing

Suicide," Ekstasis Editions, and "The Abstract of Time," Rudderless Mariner. She has been shortlisted for Vallum Magazine's Chapbook Prize for two consecutive years. Sally is an associate member of the League of Canadian Poets. Her personal blog, https://featherstone-creative.com is where she posts her back-country adventures, photos, and stories.

- Sana Mujtaba is a housewife, and mother of three beautiful kids from Pakistan. She has been writing poetry since the age of 13 and always been sensitive to the happenings around her. That led her to pick up her pen. She joined the IG community in 2019. Initially, it was fun to write for pages and prompts but now she only writes when she feels inspired. Her poetry is published in several international anthologies. Instagram @sana.m.writes

- Sanket Mhatre has been featured at Kala Ghoda Arts Festival, Poets Translating Poets, Goa Arts & Literature Festival, Jaipur Literature Festival, Vagdevi Litfest and Glass House Poetry Festival. His first book of cross-translated poems, The Coordinates Of Us won the prestigious Raza Foundation Grant after been shortlisted at IWrite2020 at Jaipur Literature Festival.

- Sarah Crabtree is a UK based writer. She has two books of short stories for adults, and two children's picture books available on Amazon, along with a non-fiction light-hearted guide for aspiring writers. Her latest story appears in the Amazon #1 Best-selling Christmas horror anthology Wight Christmas. Sarah is currently working on another short story collection for adults. "The Ghosts You Call Up" is an edited version of the story of the same name included in her 2020 self-published book, The Ghost House Collection.

- Sarah Henry is retired from a major newspaper. Her poems appear in *WINK:Writers in the Know, Bluebird Word, UniVerses, Hedge Apple Magazine* and *Trouvaille Review*. She lives and writes in a small Pennsylvania town.

- Simon J. Plant is an Aussie expat ballet dancer and fiction writer based in Cincinnati, Ohio. When he's not performing with Cincinnati Ballet he's either vacillating between synonyms or letting his husband know "we're plumb out of gin." His work has appeared in anthologies and/or magazines by *Not a Pipe Publishing, The Writer Shed, DarkLit Press, Red Cape Publishing, Hiraeth*, and others. You can learn more at: www.simonjplant.com

- Sonia Charales is a South Indian American writer and artist. Her work involves exploration of South Indian culture, multilingual ideas, the beauty of nature, and healing. Her work appears most recently in *antonym, Suspension Literary Magazine, Perfumed Pages, The Firefly Review*, and elsewhere. She is in the process of becoming an optometrist.

- Stephanie Parent is an author of horror and magical realism. Her poetry collection *Every Poem a Potion, Every Song a Spell* was released August 2022 from Querencia Press, and her debut gothic horror novel *The Briars* is forthcoming May 2023 from Cemetery Gates Media.

- Stephen Mead is an Outsider multi-media artist and writer. Since the 1990s he's been grateful to many editors for publishing his work in print zines and eventually online. He is also grateful to have managed to keep various day jobs for the Health Insurance. Currently he is resident artist/curator for The Chroma Museum, artistic renderings of LGBTQI historical figures, organizations and allies predominantly before Stonewall.

- Talya Jacoby is a London based pen-possessed poet. She has one self-published collection (a rhyme filled thing with some illustrations from yonks ago), been featured in two anthologies to date and now uses Instagram (@talyajacoby) as a dumping ground for her nonthology. She has mostly ditched the rhymes but can hardly resist wordplay, one might say she likes playing with food for thought.

- Tammy is a 26 year old South African student, poet, artist and photographer. Creativity is all she knows. Enthusiastic, passionate and opinionated, she uses each day to learn more about herself, and therefore, more about each craft. She believes in authenticity and vulnerability when writing, as it helps to connect with the reader - with the soul. So far, her poetry has been published in *Blue Daisies, Sunday Morning at the River, decurated, Colortag Magazine, Eclipse Zine* & *Pile Press,* with artwork published in *Stuck in Notes.* She's only getting started;)

- Valerie Wardh is a writer in Austin, Texas. Her poetry has appeared in *Book of Matches.* She dabbles in tarot and builds little worlds for her gecko friends.

- Valyntina is a multi-genre artist living with her wife in Tucson, AZ. She works with paint, ink, Neon, encaustic medium, recycled or repurposed materials and words. She is the author of two poetry chapbooks, *Fever Dream/ Take Heart* (Cathexis Northwest Press 2020) and *In Our Now* (Finishing Line Press 2022). You'll find her work in *Impermanent Earth, The Journal, Lana Turner* and *The Night Heron Barks.* Find her at valyntinagrenier.com or Insta @valyntinagrenier.

CPSIA information can be obtained
at www.ICGtesting.com
Printed in the USA
BVHW031024311022
650751BV00012B/105